Goosebumps®

VANISHING COLLECTION

SAY CHEESE AND DIE!
THE CURSE OF THE MUMMY'S TOMB
LET'S GET INVISIBLE!

R.L. STINE

SCHOLASTIC INC.

New York Toronto London Auckland Sydney
Mexico City New Delhi Hong Kong Buenos Aires

The Goosebumps book series created by Parachute Press, Inc.

ISBN 0-681-02519-0

Say Cheese and Die!, ISBN 0-439-56842-0,
copyright © 1992 by Scholastic Inc.

The Curse of the Mummy's Tomb, ISBN 0-439-56827-7,
copyright © 1993 by Scholastic Inc.

Let's Get Invisible!, ISBN 0-439-56838-2,
copyright © 1993 by Scholastic Inc.

12 11 10 9 8 7 6 5 4 3 2 1   4 5 6 7 8 9/0

Printed in the U.S.A.   40

First compilation printing, November 2004

CONTENTS

SAY CHEESE AND DIE!

1

"There's nothing to do in Pitts Landing," Michael Warner said, his hands shoved into the pockets of his faded denim cutoffs.

"Yeah. Pitts Landing is the pits," Greg Banks said.

Doug Arthur and Shari Walker muttered their agreement.

Pitts Landing is the Pits. That was the town slogan, according to Greg and his three friends. Actually, Pitts Landing wasn't much different from a lot of small towns with quiet streets of shady lawns and comfortable, old houses.

But here it was, a balmy fall afternoon, and the four friends were hanging around Greg's driveway, kicking at the gravel, wondering what to do for fun and excitement.

"Let's go to Grover's and see if the new comic books have come in," Doug suggested.

"We don't have any money, Bird," Greg told him.

Everyone called Doug "Bird" because he looked

a lot like a bird. A better nickname might have been "Stork." He had long, skinny legs and took long, storklike steps. Under his thick tuft of brown hair, which he seldom brushed, he had small, birdlike brown eyes and a long nose that curved like a beak. Doug didn't really like being called Bird, but he was used to it.

"We can still *look* at the comics," Bird insisted.

"Until Grover starts yelling at you," Shari said. She puffed out her cheeks and did a pretty good imitation of the gruff store owner: *"Are you paying or staying?"*

"He thinks he's cool," Greg said, laughing at her imitation. "He's such a jerk."

"I think the new *X-Force* is coming in this week," Bird said.

"You should join the X-Force," Greg said, giving his pal a playful shove. "You could be Bird Man. You'd be great!"

"We should *all* join the X-Force," Michael said. "If we were super-heroes, maybe we'd have something to do."

"No, we wouldn't," Shari quickly replied. "There's no crime to fight in Pitts Landing."

"We could fight crabgrass," Bird suggested. He was the joker in the group.

The others laughed. The four of them had been friends for a long time. Greg and Shari lived next door to each other, and their parents were best friends. Bird and Michael lived on the next block.

"How about a baseball game?" Michael suggested. "We could go down to the playground."

"No way," Shari said. "You can't play with only four people." She pushed back a strand of her crimped, black hair that had fallen over her face. Shari was wearing an oversized yellow sweatshirt over bright green leggings.

"Maybe we'll find some other kids there," Michael said, picking up a handful of gravel from the drive and letting it sift through his chubby fingers. Michael had short red hair, blue eyes, and a face full of freckles. He wasn't exactly fat, but no one would ever call him skinny.

"Come on, let's play baseball," Bird urged. "I need the practice. My Little League starts in a couple of days."

"Little League? In the fall?" Shari asked.

"It's a new fall league. The first game is Tuesday after school," Bird explained.

"Hey — we'll come watch you," Greg said.

"We'll come watch you strike out," Shari added. Her hobby was teasing Bird.

"What position are you playing?" Greg asked.

"Backstop," Michael cracked.

No one laughed. Michael's jokes always fell flat.

Bird shrugged. "Probably the outfield. How come *you're* not playing, Greg?"

With his big shoulders and muscular arms and legs, Greg was the natural athlete of the group. He was blond and good-looking, with flashing

3

gray-green eyes and a wide, friendly smile.

"My brother Terry was supposed to go sign me up, but he forgot," Greg said, making a disgusted face.

"Where *is* Terry?" Shari asked. She had a tiny crush on Greg's older brother.

"He got a job Saturdays and after school. At the Dairy Freeze," Greg told her.

"Let's go to the Dairy Freeze!" Michael exclaimed enthusiastically.

"We don't have any money — remember?" Bird said glumly.

"Terry'll give us free cones," Michael said, turning a hopeful gaze on Greg.

"Yeah. Free cones. But no ice cream in them," Greg told him. "You know what a straight-arrow my brother is."

"This is boring," Shari complained, watching a robin hop across the sidewalk. "It's boring standing around talking about how bored we are."

"We could *sit down* and talk about how bored we are," Bird suggested, twisting his mouth into the goofy half-smile he always wore when he was making a dumb joke.

"Let's take a walk or a jog or something," Shari insisted. She made her way across the lawn and began walking, balancing her white high-tops on the edge of the curb, waving her arms like a high-wire performer.

The boys followed, imitating her in an impromptu game of Follow the Leader, all of them balancing on the curb edge as they walked.

A curious cocker spaniel came bursting out of the neighbors' hedge, yapping excitedly. Shari stopped to pet him. The dog, its stub of a tail wagging furiously, licked her hand a few times. Then the dog lost interest and disappeared back into the hedge.

The four friends continued down the block, playfully trying to knock each other off the curb as they walked. They crossed the street and continued on past the school. A couple of guys were shooting baskets, and some little kids played kickball on the practice baseball diamond, but no one they knew.

The road curved away from the school. They followed it past familiar houses. Then, just beyond a small wooded area, they stopped and looked up a sloping lawn, the grass uncut for weeks, tall weeds poking out everywhere, the shrubs ragged and overgrown.

At the top of the lawn, nearly hidden in the shadows of enormous, old oak trees, sprawled a large, ramshackle house. The house, anyone could see, had once been grand. It was gray shingle, three stories tall, with a wraparound screened porch, a sloping red roof, and tall chimneys on either end. But the broken windows on the second floor, the cracked, weather-stained shingles, the bare spots on the roof, and the shutters hanging loosely beside the dust-smeared windows were evidence of the house's neglect.

Everyone in Pitts Landing knew it as the Coffman house. Coffman was the name painted on the mailbox that tilted on its broken pole over the front walk.

But the house had been deserted for years — ever since Greg and his friends could remember.

And people liked to tell weird stories about the house: ghost stories and wild tales about murders and ghastly things that happened there. Most likely, none of them were true.

"Hey — I know what we can do for excitement," Michael said, staring up at the house bathed in shadows.

"Huh? What are you talking about?" Greg asked warily.

"Let's go into the Coffman house," Michael said, starting to make his way across the weed-choked lawn.

"Whoa. Are you crazy?" Greg called, hurrying to catch up to him.

"Let's go in," Michael said, his blue eyes catching the light of the late afternoon sun filtering down through the tall oak trees. "We wanted an adventure. Something a little exciting, right? Come on — let's check it out."

Greg hesitated and stared up at the house. A cold chill ran down his back.

Before he could reply, a dark form leapt up from the shadows of the tall weeds and attacked him!

2

Greg toppled backwards onto the ground. "Aah!" he screamed. Then he realized the others were laughing.

"It's that dumb cocker spaniel!" Shari cried. "He followed us!"

"Go home, dog. Go home!" Bird shooed the dog away.

The dog trotted to the curb, turned around, and stared back at them, its stubby tail wagging furiously.

Feeling embarrassed that he'd become so frightened, Greg slowly pulled himself to his feet, expecting his friends to give him grief. But they were staring up at the Coffman house thoughtfully.

"Yeah, Michael's right," Bird said, slapping Michael hard on the back, so hard Michael winced and turned to slug Bird. "Let's see what it's like in there."

"No way," Greg said, hanging back. "I mean,

the place is kind of creepy, don't you think?"

"So?" Shari challenged him, joining Michael and Bird, who repeated her question: "So?"

"So . . . I don't know," Greg replied. He didn't like being the sensible one of the group. Everyone always made fun of the sensible one. He'd rather be the wild and crazy one. But, somehow, he always ended up sensible.

"I don't think we should go in there," he said, staring up at the neglected old house.

"Are you chicken?" Bird asked.

"Chicken!" Michael joined in.

Bird began to cluck loudly, tucking his hands into his armpits and flapping his arms. With his beady eyes and beaky nose, he looked just like a chicken.

Greg didn't want to laugh, but he couldn't help it.

Bird *always* made him laugh.

The clucking and flapping seemed to end the discussion. They were standing at the foot of the broken concrete steps that led up to the screened porch.

"Look. The window next to the front door is broken," Shari said. "We can just reach in and open the door."

"This is cool," Michael said enthusiastically.

"Are we really doing this?" Greg, being the sensible one, had to ask. "I mean — what about Spidey?"

Spidey was a weird-looking man of fifty or sixty they'd all seen lurking about town. He dressed entirely in black and crept along on long, slender legs. He looked just like a black spider, so the kids all called him Spidey.

Most likely he was a homeless guy. No one really knew anything about him — where he'd come from, where he lived. But a lot of kids had seen him hanging around the Coffman house.

"Maybe Spidey doesn't like visitors," Greg warned.

But Shari was already reaching in through the broken windowpane to unlock the front door. And after little effort, she turned the brass knob and the heavy wooden door swung open.

One by one, they stepped into the front entryway, Greg reluctantly bringing up the rear. It was dark inside the house. Only narrow beams of sunlight managed to trickle down through the heavy trees in front, creating pale circles of light on the worn brown carpet at their feet.

The floorboards squeaked as Greg and his friends made their way past the living room, which was bare except for a couple of overturned grocery store cartons against one wall.

Spidey's furniture? Greg wondered.

The living room carpet, as threadbare as the one in the entryway, had a dark oval stain in the center of it. Greg and Bird, stopping in the doorway, both noticed it at the same time.

"Think it's blood?" Bird asked, his tiny eyes lighting up with excitement.

Greg felt a chill on the back of his neck. "Probably ketchup," he replied. Bird laughed and slapped him hard on the back.

Shari and Michael were exploring the kitchen. They were staring at the dust-covered kitchen counter as Greg stepped up behind them. He saw immediately what had captured their attention. Two fat, gray mice were standing on the countertop, staring back at them.

"They're cute," Shari said. "They look just like cartoon mice."

The sound of her voice made the two rodents scamper along the counter, around the sink, and out of sight.

"They're gross," Michael said, making a disgusted face. "I think they were rats — not mice."

"Rats have long tails. Mice don't," Greg told him.

"They were definitely rats," Bird muttered, pushing past them and into the hallway. He disappeared toward the front of the house.

Shari reached up and pulled open a cabinet over the counter. Empty. "I guess Spidey never uses the kitchen," she said.

"Well, I didn't *think* he was a gourmet chef," Greg joked.

He followed her into the long, narrow dining room, as bare and dusty as the other rooms. A low chandelier still hung from the ceiling, so brown with caked dust, it was impossible to tell that it was glass.

"Looks like a haunted house," Greg said softly.

"Boo," Shari replied.

"There's not much to see in here," Greg complained, following her back to the dark hallway. "Unless you get a thrill from dustballs."

Suddenly, a loud *crack* made him jump.

Shari laughed and squeezed his shoulder.

"What was *that*?" he cried, unable to stifle his fear.

"Old houses *do* things like that," she said. "They make noises for no reason at all."

"I think we should leave," Greg insisted, embarrassed again that he'd acted so frightened. "I mean, it's boring in here."

"It's kind of exciting being somewhere we're not supposed to be," Shari said, peeking into a dark, empty room — probably a den or study at one time.

"I guess," Greg replied uncertainly.

They bumped into Michael. "Where's Bird?" Greg asked.

"I think he went down in the basement," Michael replied.

"Huh? The basement?"

Michael pointed to an open door at the right of the hallway. "The stairs are there."

The three of them made their way to the top of

11

the stairs. They peered down into the darkness. "Bird?"

From somewhere deep in the basement, his voice floated up to them in a horrified scream: "Help! It's got me! Somebody — please help! It's *got* me!"

3

"It's got me! It's got me!"

At the sound of Bird's terrified cries, Greg pushed past Shari and Michael, who stood frozen in open-mouthed horror. Practically flying down the steep stairway, Greg called out to his friend. "I'm coming, Bird! What *is* it?"

His heart pounding, Greg stopped at the bottom of the stairs, every muscle tight with fear. His eyes searched frantically through the smoky light pouring in from the basement windows up near the ceiling.

"Bird?"

There he was, sitting comfortably, calmly, on an overturned metal trash can, his legs crossed, a broad smile on his birdlike face. "Gotcha," he said softly, and burst out laughing.

"What *is* it? What *happened*?" came the frightened voices of Shari and Michael. They clamored down the stairs, coming to a stop beside Greg.

It took them only a few seconds to scope out the situation.

"Another dumb joke?" Michael asked, his voice still trembling with fear.

"Bird — you were goofing on us again?" Shari asked, shaking her head.

Enjoying his moment, Bird nodded, with his peculiar half-grin. "You guys are too easy," he scoffed.

"But, Doug — " Shari started. She only called him Doug when she was upset with him. "Haven't you ever heard of the boy who cried wolf? What if something bad happens sometime, and you really need help, and we think you're just goofing?"

"What could happen?" Bird replied smugly. He stood up and gestured around the basement. "Look — it's brighter down here than upstairs."

He was right. Sunlight from the back yard cascaded down through four long windows at ground level, near the ceiling of the basement.

"I still think we should get out of here," Greg insisted, his eyes moving quickly around the large, cluttered room.

Behind Bird's overturned trash can stood an improvised table made out of a sheet of plywood resting on four paint cans. A nearly flat mattress, dirty and stained, rested against the wall, a faded wool blanket folded at the foot.

"Spidey must *live* down here!" Michael exclaimed.

Bird kicked his way through a pile of empty food boxes that had been tossed all over the floor — TV dinners, mostly. "Hey, a Hungry Man dinner!" he exclaimed. "Where does Spidey heat these up?"

"Maybe he eats them frozen," Shari suggested. "You know. Like Popsicles."

She made her way toward a towering oak wardrobe and pulled open the doors. "Wow! This is *excellent!*" she declared. "Look!" She pulled out a ratty-looking fur coat and wrapped it around her shoulders. "Excellent!" she repeated, twirling in the old coat.

From across the room, Greg could see that the wardrobe was stuffed with old clothing. Michael and Bird hurried to join Shari and began pulling out strange-looking pairs of bell-bottom pants, yellowed dress shirts with pleats down the front, tie-dyed neckties that were about a foot wide, and bright-colored scarves and bandannas.

"Hey, guys — " Greg warned. "Don't you think maybe those belong to somebody?"

Bird spun around, a fuzzy red boa wrapped around his neck and shoulders. "Yeah. These are Spidey's dress-up clothes," he cracked.

"Check out this *baad* hat," Shari said, turning around to show off the bright purple, wide-brimmed hat she had pulled on.

"Neat," Michael said, examining a long blue cape. "This stuff must be at least twenty-five years old. It's awesome. How could someone just leave it here?"

"Maybe they're coming back for it," Greg suggested.

As his friends explored the contents of the wardrobe, Greg wandered to the other end of the large basement. A furnace occupied the far wall, its ducts covered in thick cobwebs. Partially hidden by the furnace ducts, Greg could see stairs, probably leading to an outside exit.

Wooden shelves lined the adjoining wall, cluttered with old paint cans, rags, newspapers, and rusty tools.

Whoever lived here must have been a real handyman, Greg thought, examining a wooden worktable in front of the shelves. A metal vise was clamped to the edge of the worktable. Greg turned the handle, expecting the jaws of the vise to open.

But to his surprise, as he turned the vise handle, a door just above the worktable popped open. Greg pulled the door all the way open, revealing a hidden cabinet shelf.

Resting on the shelf was a camera.

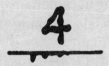

4

For a long moment, Greg just stared at the camera.

Something told him the camera was hidden away for a reason.

Something told him he shouldn't touch it. He should close the secret door and walk away.

But he couldn't resist it.

He reached onto the hidden shelf and took the camera in his hands.

It pulled out easily. Then, to Greg's surprise, the door instantly snapped shut with a loud *bang*.

Weird, he thought, turning the camera in his hands.

What a strange place to leave a camera. Why would someone put it here? If it were valuable enough to hide in a secret cabinet, why didn't they take it with them?

Greg eagerly examined the camera. It was large and surprisingly heavy, with a long lens. Perhaps a telephoto lens, he thought.

Greg was very interested in cameras. He had an inexpensive automatic camera, which took okay snapshots. But he was saving his allowance in hopes of buying a really good camera with a lot of lenses.

He loved looking at camera magazines, studying the different models, picking out the ones he wanted to buy.

Sometimes he daydreamed about traveling around the world, going to amazing places, mountaintops and hidden jungle rivers. He'd take photos of everything he saw and become a famous photographer.

His camera at home was just too crummy. That's why all his pictures came out too dark or too light, and everyone in them had glowing red dots in their eyes.

Greg wondered if this camera was any good.

Raising the viewfinder to his eye, he sighted around the room. He came to a stop on Michael, who was wearing two bright yellow feather boas and a white Stetson hat and had climbed to the top of the steps to pose.

"Wait! Hold it!" Greg cried, moving closer, raising the camera to his eye. "Let me take your picture, Michael."

"Where'd you find that?" Bird asked.

"Does that thing have film in it?" Michael demanded.

"I don't know," Greg said. "Let's see."

Leaning against the railing, Michael struck what he considered a sophisticated pose.

Greg pointed the camera up and focused carefully. It took a short while for his finger to locate the shutter button. "Okay, ready? Say cheese."

"Cheddar," Michael said, grinning down at Greg as he held his pose against the railing.

"Very funny. Michael's a riot," Bird said sarcastically.

Greg centered Michael in the viewfinder frame, then pressed the shutter button.

The camera clicked and flashed.

Then it made an electronic whirring sound. A slot pulled open on the bottom, and a cardboard square slid out.

"Hey — it's one of those automatic-developing cameras," Greg exclaimed. He pulled the square of cardboard out and examined it. "Look — the picture is starting to develop."

"Let me see," Michael called down, leaning on the railing.

But before he could start down the stairs, everyone heard a loud crunching sound.

They all looked up to the source of the sound — and saw the railing break away and Michael go sailing over the edge.

"Noooooo!" Michael screamed as he toppled to the floor, arms outstretched, the feather boas flying behind him like animal tails.

He turned in the air, then hit the concrete hard

on his back, his eyes frozen wide in astonishment and fright.

He bounced once.

Then cried out again: "My ankle! Owwww! My ankle!" He grabbed at the injured ankle, then quickly let go with a loud gasp. It hurt too much to touch it.

"*Ohhh* — my ankle!"

Still holding the camera and the photo, Greg rushed to Michael. Shari and Bird did the same.

"We'll go get help," Shari told Michael, who was still on his back, groaning in pain.

But then they heard the ceiling creak.

Footsteps. Above them.

Someone was in the house.

Someone was approaching the basement stairs.

They were going to be caught.

5

The footsteps overhead grew louder.

The four friends exchanged frightened glances. "We've got to get *out* of here," Shari whispered.

The ceiling creaked.

"You can't leave me here!" Michael protested. He pulled himself to a sitting position.

"Quick — stand up," Bird instructed.

Michael struggled to his feet. "I can't stand on this foot." His face revealed his panic.

"We'll help you," Shari said, turning her eyes to Bird. "I'll take one arm. You take the other."

Bird obediently moved forward and pulled Michael's arm around his shoulder.

"Okay, let's move!" Shari whispered, supporting Michael from the other side.

"But how do we get out?" Bird asked breathlessly.

The footsteps grew louder. The ceiling creaked under their weight.

"We can't go up the stairs," Michael whispered, leaning on Shari and Bird.

"There's another stairway behind the furnace," Greg told them, pointing.

"It leads out?" Michael asked, wincing from his ankle pain.

"Probably."

Greg led the way. "Just pray the door isn't padlocked or something."

"We're praying. We're praying!" Bird declared.

"We're outta here!" Shari said, groaning under the weight of Michael's arm.

Leaning heavily against Shari and Bird, Michael hobbled after Greg, and they made their way to the stairs behind the furnace. The stairs, they saw, led to wooden double doors up on ground level.

"I don't see a padlock," Greg said warily. "Please, doors — be open!"

"*Hey — who's down there?*" an angry man's voice called from behind them.

"It's — it's Spidey!" Michael stammered.

"Hurry!" Shari urged, giving Greg a frightened push. "Come *on!*"

Greg set the camera down on the top step. Then he reached up and grabbed the handles of the double doors.

"*Who's down there?*"

Spidey sounded closer, angrier.

"The doors could be locked from the outside," Greg whispered, hesitating.

"Just *push* them, man!" Bird pleaded.

Greg took a deep breath and pushed with all his strength.

The doors didn't budge.

"We're trapped," he told them.

6

"Now what?" Michael whined.

"Try again," Bird urged Greg. "Maybe they're just stuck." He slid out from under Michael's arm. "Here. I'll help you."

Greg moved over to give Bird room to step up beside him. "Ready?" he asked. "One, two, three — *push!*"

Both boys pushed against the heavy wooden doors with all their might.

And the doors swung open.

"Okay! *Now* we're outta here!" Shari declared happily.

Picking up the camera, Greg led the way out. The back yard, he saw, was as weed-choked and overgrown as the front. An enormous limb had fallen off an old oak tree, probably during a storm, and was lying half in the tree, half on the ground.

Somehow, Bird and Shari managed to drag Michael up the steps and onto the grass. "Can you walk? Try it," Bird said.

Still leaning against the two of them, Michael reluctantly pushed his foot down on the ground. He lifted it. Then pushed it again. "Hey, it feels a little better," he said, surprised.

"Then let's go," Bird said.

They ran to the overgrown hedge that edged along the side of the yard, Michael on his own now, stepping gingerly on the bad ankle, doing his best to keep up. Then, staying in the shadow of the hedge, they made their way around the house to the front.

"All *right!*" Bird cried happily as they reached the street. "We made it!"

Gasping for breath, Greg stopped at the curb and turned back toward the house. "Look!" he cried, pointing up to the living room window.

A dark figure stood in the window, hands pressed against the glass.

"It's Spidey," Shari said.

"He's just — staring at us," Michael cried.

"Weird," Greg said. "Let's go."

They didn't stop till they got to Michael's house, a sprawling redwood ranch-style house behind a shady front lawn.

"How's the ankle?" Greg asked.

"It's loosened up a lot. It doesn't even hurt that much," Michael said.

"Man, you could've been *killed*!" Bird declared, wiping sweat off his forehead with the sleeve of his T-shirt.

"Thanks for reminding me," Michael said dryly.

"Lucky thing you've got all that extra padding," Bird teased.

"Shut up," Michael muttered.

"Well, you guys wanted adventure," Shari said, leaning back against the trunk of a tree.

"That guy Spidey is definitely weird," Bird said, shaking his head.

"You see the way he was staring at us?" Michael asked. "All dressed in black and everything? He looked like some kind of zombie or something."

"He saw us," Greg said softly, suddenly feeling a chill of dread. "He saw us very clearly. We'd better stay away from there."

"What for?" Michael demanded. "It isn't his house. He's just sleeping there. We could call the police on him."

"But if he's really crazy or something, there's no telling what he might do," Greg replied thoughtfully.

"Aw, he's not going to do anything," Shari said quietly. "Spidey doesn't want trouble. He just wants to be left alone."

"Yeah," Michael agreed quickly. "He didn't want us messing with his stuff. That's why he yelled like that and came after us."

Michael was leaning over, rubbing his ankle.

"Hey, where's my picture?" he demanded, straightening up and turning to Greg.

"Huh?"

"You know. The picture you snapped. With the camera."

"Oh. Right." Greg suddenly realized he still had the camera gripped tightly in his hand. He set it down carefully on the grass and reached into his back pocket. "I put it in here when we started to run," he explained.

"Well? Did it come out?" Michael demanded.

The three of them huddled around Greg to get a view of the snapshot.

"Whoa — hold on a minute!" Greg cried, staring hard at the small, square photo. "Something's wrong. What's going *on* here?"

7

The four friends gaped at the photograph in Greg's hand, their mouths dropping open in surprise.

The camera had caught Michael in midair as he fell through the broken railing to the floor.

"That's impossible!" Shari cried.

"You snapped the picture *before* I fell!" Michael declared, grabbing the photo out of Greg's hand so that he could study it close up. "I remember it."

"You remembered wrong," Bird said, moving to get another look at it over Michael's shoulder. "You were falling, man. What a great action shot." He picked up the camera. "This is a good camera you stole, Greg."

"I didn't steal it" — Greg started — "I mean, I didn't realize — "

"I wasn't falling!" Michael insisted, tilting the picture in his hand, studying it from every angle. "I was posing, remember? I had a big, goofy smile on my face, and I was posing."

28

"I remember the goofy smile," Bird said, handing the camera back to Greg. "Do you have any *other* expression?"

"You're not funny, Bird," Michael muttered. He pocketed the picture.

"Weird," Greg said. He glanced at his watch. "Hey — I've got to get going."

He said good-bye to the others and headed for home. The afternoon sun was lowering behind a cluster of palm trees, casting long, shifting shadows over the sidewalk.

He had promised his mother he'd straighten up his room and help with the vacuuming before dinner. And now he was late.

What was that strange car in the drive? he wondered, jogging across the neighbor's lawn toward his house.

It was a navy-blue Taurus station wagon. Brand new.

Dad picked up our new car! he realized.

Wow! Greg stopped to admire it. It still had the sticker glued to the door window. He pulled open the driver's door, leaned in, and smelled the vinyl upholstery.

Mmmmmm. That new-car smell.

He inhaled deeply again. It smelled so good. So fresh and new.

He closed the door hard, appreciating the solid *clunk* it made as it closed.

What a great new car, he thought excitedly.

He raised the camera to his eye and took a few steps back off the drive.

I've *got* to take a picture of this, he thought. To remember what the car was like when it was totally new.

He backed up until he had framed the entire profile of the station wagon in the viewfinder. Then he pressed the shutter button.

As before, the camera clicked loudly, the flash flashed, and with an electronic *whirr*, a square undeveloped photo of gray and yellow slid out of the bottom.

Carrying the camera and the snapshot, Greg ran into the house through the front door. "I'm home!" he called. "Down in a minute!" And hurried up the carpeted stairs to his room.

"Greg? Is that you? Your father is home," his mother called from downstairs.

"I know. Be right down. Sorry I'm late!" Greg shouted back.

I'd better hide the camera, he decided. If Mom or Dad see it, they'll want to know whose it is and where I got it. And I won't be able to answer those questions.

"Greg — did you see the new car? Are you coming down?" his mother called impatiently from the foot of the stairs.

"I'm coming!" he yelled.

His eyes searched frantically for a good hiding place.

Under his bed?

No. His mom might vacuum under there and discover it.

Then Greg remembered the secret compartment in his headboard. He had discovered the compartment years ago when his parents had bought him a new bedroom set. Quickly, he shoved the camera in.

Peering into the mirror above his dresser, he gave his blond hair a quick brush, rubbed a black soot smudge off his cheek with one hand, then started for the door.

He stopped at the doorway.

The snapshot of the car. Where had he put it?

It took a few seconds to remember that he had tossed it onto his bed. Curious about how it came out, he turned back to retrieve it.

"Oh, no!"

He uttered a low cry as he gazed at the snapshot.

8

What's going on here? Greg wondered.

He brought the photo up close to his face.

This isn't right, he thought. How can this *be*?

The blue Taurus station wagon in the photo was
a mess. It looked as if it had been in a terrible
accident. The windshield was shattered. Metal
was twisted and bent. The door on the driver's
side was caved in.

The car appeared *totaled*!

"This is impossible!" Greg uttered aloud.

"Greg, where *are* you?" his mother called.
"We're all hungry, and you're keeping us waiting."

"Sorry," he answered, unable to take his eyes
off the snapshot. "Coming."

He shoved the photo into his top dresser drawer
and made his way downstairs. The image of the
totaled car burned in his mind.

Just to make sure, he crossed the living room

and peeked out of the front window to the drive-way.

There stood the station wagon, sparkling in the glow of the setting sun. Shiny and perfect.

He turned and walked into the dining room where his brother and his parents were already seated. "The new wagon is awesome, Dad," Greg said, trying to shake the snapshot's image from his thoughts.

But he kept seeing the twisted metal, the caved-in driver's door, the shattered windshield.

"After dinner," Greg's dad announced happily, "I'm taking you all for a drive in the new car!"

9

"Mmmm. This is great chicken, Mom," Greg's brother Terry said, chewing as he talked.

"Thanks for the compliment," Mrs. Banks said dryly, "but it's veal — not chicken."

Greg and his dad burst out laughing. Terry's face grew bright red. "Well," he said, still chewing, "it's such excellent veal, it tastes as good as chicken!"

"I don't know why I bother to cook," Mrs. Banks sighed.

Mr. Banks changed the subject. "How are things at the Dairy Freeze?" he asked.

"We ran out of vanilla this afternoon," Terry said, forking a small potato and shoving it whole into his mouth. He chewed it briefly, then gulped it down. "People were annoyed about that."

"I don't think I can go for the ride," Greg said, staring down at his dinner, which he'd hardly touched. "I mean — "

"Why not?" his father asked.

"Well . . ." Greg searched his mind for a good reason. He needed to make one up, but his mind was a blank.

He couldn't tell them the truth.

That he had taken a snapshot of Michael, and it showed Michael falling. Then a few seconds later, Michael had fallen.

And now he had taken a picture of the new car. And the car was wrecked in the photo.

Greg didn't really know what it meant. But he was suddenly filled with this powerful feeling, of dread, of fear, of . . . he didn't know what.

A kind of troubled feeling he'd never had before.

But he couldn't tell them any of that. It was too weird. Too *crazy*.

"I . . . made plans to go over to Michael's," he lied, staring down at his plate.

"Well, call him and tell him you'll see him tomorrow," Mr. Banks said, slicing his veal. "That's no problem."

"Well, I'm kind of not feeling very well, either," Greg said.

"What's wrong?" Mrs. Banks asked with instant concern. "Do you have a temperature? I thought you looked a little flushed when you came in."

"No," Greg replied uncomfortably. "No temperature. I just feel kind of tired, not very hungry."

"Can I have your chicken — I mean, veal?" Terry asked eagerly. He reached his fork across the table and nabbed the cutlet off Greg's plate.

"Well, a nice ride might make you feel better," Greg's dad said, eyeing Greg suspiciously. "You know, some fresh air. You can stretch out in the back if you want."

"But, Dad — " Greg stopped. He had used up all the excuses he could think of. They would *never* believe him if he said he needed to stay home and do homework on a Saturday night!

"You're coming with us, and that's final," Mr. Banks said, still studying Greg closely. "You've been dying for this new wagon to arrive. I really don't understand your problem."

Neither do I, Greg admitted to himself.

I don't understand it at all. Why am I so afraid of riding in the new car? Just because there's something wrong with that stupid camera?

I'm being silly, Greg thought, trying to shake away the feeling of dread that had taken away his appetite.

"'Okay, Dad, Great," he said, forcing a smile. "I'll come."

"Are there any more potatoes?" Terry asked.

10

"It's so easy to drive," Mr. Banks said, accelerating onto the entry ramp to the freeway. "It handles like a small car, not like a station wagon."

"Plenty of room back here, Dad," Terry said, scooting low in the back seat beside Greg, raising his knees to the back of the front seat.

"Hey, look — there's a drink holder that pulls out from the dash!" Greg's mother exclaimed. "That's neat."

"Awesome, Mom," Terry said sarcastically.

"Well, we never had a drink holder before," Mrs. Banks replied. She turned back to the two boys. "Are your seat belts buckled? Do they work properly?"

"Yeah. They're okay," Terry replied.

"They checked them at the showroom, before I took the car," Mr. Banks said, signaling to move into the left lane.

A truck roared by, spitting a cloud of exhaust behind it. Greg stared out the front window. His door window was still covered by the new car sticker.

Mr. Banks pulled off the freeway, onto a nearly empty four-lane highway that curved toward the west. The setting sun was a red ball low on the horizon in a charcoal-gray sky.

"Put the pedal to the metal, Dad," Terry urged, sitting up and leaning forward. "Let's see what this car can do."

Mr. Banks obediently pressed his foot on the accelerator. "The cruising speed seems to be about sixty," he said.

"Slow down," Mrs. Banks scolded. "You know the speed limit is fifty-five."

"I'm just testing it," Greg's dad said defensively. "You know. Making sure the transmission doesn't slip or anything."

Greg stared at the glowing speedometer. They were doing seventy now.

"Slow down. I mean it," Mrs. Banks insisted. "You're acting like a crazy teenager."

"That's me!" Mr. Banks replied, laughing. "This is *awesome!*" he said, imitating Terry, ignoring his wife's pleas to slow down.

They roared past a couple of small cars in the right lane. Headlights of cars moving towards them were a bright white blur in the darkening night.

"Hey, Greg, you've been awfully quiet," his mother said. "You feeling okay?"

"Yeah. I'm okay," Greg said softly.

He wished his dad would slow down. He was doing seventy-five now.

"What do you think, Greg?" Mr. Banks asked, steering with his left hand as his right hand searched the dashboard. "Where's the light switch? I should turn on my headlights."

"The car's great," Greg replied, trying to sound enthusiastic. But he couldn't shake away the fear, couldn't get the photo of the mangled car out of his mind.

"Where's that stupid light switch? It's got to be here somewhere," Mr. Banks said.

As he glanced down at the unfamiliar dashboard, the station wagon swerved to the left.

"Dad — look out for that truck!" Greg screamed.

11

Horns blared.

A powerful blast of air swept over the station wagon, like a giant ocean wave pushing it to the side.

Mr. Banks swerved the station wagon to the right.

The truck rumbled past.

"Sorry," Greg's dad said, eyes straight ahead, slowing the car to sixty, fifty-five, fifty . . .

"I *told* you to slow down," Mrs. Banks scolded, shaking her head. "We could've been killed!"

"I was trying to find the lights," he explained. "Oh. Here they are. On the steering wheel." He clicked on the headlights.

"You boys okay?" Mrs. Banks asked, turning to check them out.

"Yeah. Fine," Terry said, sounding a little shaken. The truck would have hit his side of the car.

"I'm okay," Greg said. "Can we go back now?"

"Don't you want to keep going?" Mr. Banks asked, unable to hide his disappointment. "I thought we'd keep going to Santa Clara. Stop and get some ice cream or something."

"Greg's right," Mrs. Banks said softly to her husband. "Enough for tonight, dear. Let's turn around."

"The truck didn't come *that* close," Mr. Banks argued. But he obediently turned off the highway and they headed for home.

Later, safe and sound up in his room, Greg took the photograph out of his dresser and examined it. There was the new station wagon, the driver's side caved in, the windshield shattered.

"Weird," he said aloud, and placed the photo in the secret compartment in his headboard where he had stashed the camera. "Definitely weird."

He pulled the camera out of its hiding place and turned it around in his hands.

I'll try it one more time, he decided.

He walked to his dresser and aimed at the mirror above it.

I'll take a picture of myself in the mirror, he thought.

He raised the camera, then changed his mind. That won't work, he realized. The flash will reflect back and spoil the photo.

Gripping the camera in one hand, he made his way across the hall to Terry's room. His brother was at his desk, typing away on his computer

41

keyboard, his face bathed in the blue light of the monitor screen.

"Terry, can I take your picture?" Greg asked meekly, holding up the camera.

Terry typed some more, then looked up from the screen. "Hey — where'd you get the camera?"

"Uh . . . Shari loaned it to me," Greg told him, thinking quickly. Greg didn't like to lie. But he didn't feel like explaining to Terry how he and his friends had sneaked into the Coffman house and he had made off with the camera.

"So can I take your picture?" Greg asked.

"I'll probably break your camera," Terry joked.

"I think it's already broken," Greg told him. "That's why I want to test it on you."

"Go ahead," Terry said. He stuck out his tongue and crossed his eyes.

Greg snapped the shutter. An undeveloped photo slid out of the slot in front.

"Thanks. See you." Greg headed to the door.

"Hey — don't I get to see it?" Terry called after him.

"If it comes out," Greg said, and hurried across the hall to his room.

He sat down on the edge of the bed. Holding the photo in his lap, he stared at it intently as it developed. The yellows filled in first. Then the reds appeared, followed by shades of blue.

"Whoa," Greg muttered as his brother's face

came into view. "There's something definitely wrong here."

In the photo, Terry's eyes weren't crossed, and his tongue wasn't sticking out. His expression was grim, frightened. He looked very upset.

As the background came into focus, Greg had another surprise. Terry wasn't in his room. He was outdoors. There were trees in the background. And a house.

Greg stared at the house. It looked so familiar.

Was that the house across the street from the playground?

He took one more look at Terry's frightened expression. Then he tucked the photo and the camera into his secret headboard compartment and carefully closed it.

The camera must be broken, he decided, getting changed for bed.

It was the best explanation he could come up with.

Lying in bed, staring up at the shifting shadows on the ceiling, he decided not to think about it anymore.

A broken camera wasn't worth worrying about.

Tuesday afternoon after school, Greg hurried to meet Shari at the playground to watch Bird's Little League game.

It was a warm fall afternoon, the sun high in a

cloudless sky. The outfield grass had been freshly mowed and filled the air with its sharp, sweet smell.

Greg crossed the grass and squinted into the bright sunlight, searching for Shari. Both teams were warming up on the sides of the diamond, yelling and laughing, the sound of balls popping into gloves competing with their loud voices.

A few parents and several kids had come to watch. Some were standing around, some sitting in the low bleachers along the first base line.

Greg spotted Shari behind the backstop and waved to her. "Did you bring the camera?" she asked eagerly, running over to greet him.

He held it up.

"Excellent," she exclaimed, grinning. She reached for it.

"I think it's broken," Greg said, holding on to the camera. "The photos just don't come out right. It's hard to explain."

"Maybe it's not the photos. Maybe it's the photographer," Shari teased.

"Maybe I'll take a photo of you getting a knuckle sandwich," Greg threatened. He raised the camera to his eye and pointed it at her.

"Snap that, and I'll take a picture of you *eating* the camera," Shari threatened playfully. She reached up quickly and pulled the camera from his hand.

"What do you want it for, anyway?" Greg asked, making a halfhearted attempt to grab it back.

Shari held it away from his outstretched hand. "I want to take Bird's picture when he comes to bat. He looks just like an ostrich at the plate."

"I heard that." Bird appeared beside them, pretending to be insulted.

He looked ridiculous in his starched white uniform. The shirt was too big, and the pants were too short. The cap was the only thing that fit. It was blue, with a silver dolphin over the bill and the words: PITTS LANDING DOLPHINS.

"What kind of name is 'Dolphins' for a baseball team?" Greg asked, grabbing the bill and turning the cap backwards on Bird's head.

"All the other caps were taken," Bird answered. "We had a choice between the Zephyrs and the Dolphins. None of us knew what Zephyrs were, so we picked Dolphins."

Shari eyed him up and down. "Maybe you guys should play in your street clothes."

"Thanks for the encouragement," Bird replied. He spotted the camera and took it from her. "Hey, you brought the camera. Does it have film?"

"Yeah. I think so," Greg told him. "Let me see." He reached for the camera, but Bird swung it out of his grasp.

"Hey — are you going to share this thing, Greg?" he asked.

"Huh? What do you mean?" Greg reached again for the camera, and again Bird swung it away from him.

"I mean, we all risked our lives down in that basement getting it, right?" Bird said. "We should all share it."

"Well . . ." Greg hadn't thought about it. "I guess you're right, Bird. But I'm the one who found it. So — "

Shari grabbed the camera out of Bird's hand. "I told Greg to bring it so we could take your picture when you're up."

"As an example of good form?" Bird asked.

"As a *bad* example," Shari said.

"You guys are just jealous," Bird replied, frowning, "because I'm a natural athlete, and you can't cross the street without falling on your face." He turned the cap back around to face the front.

"Hey, Bird — get back here!" one of the coaches called from the playing field.

"I've got to go," Bird said, giving them a quick wave and starting to trot back to his teammates.

"No. Wait. Let me take a fast picture now," Greg said.

Bird stopped, turned around, and struck a pose.

"No. I'll take it," Shari insisted.

She started to raise the camera to her eye, pointing it toward Bird. And as she raised it, Greg grabbed for it.

"Let *me* take it!"

And the camera went off. Clicked and then flashed.

An undeveloped photo slid out.

"Hey, why'd you do that?" Shari asked angrily.

"Sorry," Greg said. "I didn't mean to — "

She pulled the photo out and held it in her hand. Greg and Bird came close to watch it develop.

"What the heck is *that*?" Bird cried, staring hard at the small square as the colors brightened and took shape.

"Oh, wow!" Greg cried.

The photo showed Bird sprawled unconscious on his back on the ground, his mouth twisted open, his neck bent at a frightening angle, his eyes shut tight.

12

"Hey — what's with this stupid camera?" Bird asked, grabbing the snapshot out of Shari's hand. He tilted it from side to side, squinting at it. "It's out of focus or something."

"Weird," Greg said, shaking his head.

"Hey, Bird — get over here!" the Dolphins' coach called.

"Coming!" Bird handed the picture back to Shari and jogged over to his teammates.

Whistles blew. The two teams stopped their practicing and trotted to the benches along the third base line.

"How did this *happen?*" Shari asked Greg, shielding her eyes from the sun with one hand, holding the photo close to her face with the other. "It really looks like Bird is lying on the ground, knocked out or something. But he was standing right in front of us."

"I don't get it. I really don't," Greg replied thoughtfully. "The camera keeps doing that."

Carrying the camera at his side, swinging it by its slender strap, he followed her to a shady spot beside the bleachers.

"Look how his neck is bent," Shari continued. "It's so *awful*."

"There's something definitely wrong with the camera," Greg said. He started to tell her about the snapshot he took of the new station wagon, and the snapshot of his brother Terry. But she interrupted him before he could get the words out.

" — And that picture of Michael. It showed him falling down the stairs before he even fell. It's just so strange."

"I know," Greg agreed.

"Let me see that thing," Shari said and pulled the camera from his hand. "Is there any film left?"

"I can't tell," Greg admitted. "I couldn't find a film counter or anything."

Shari examined the camera closely, rolling it over in her hands. "It doesn't say anywhere. How can you tell if it's loaded or not?"

Greg shrugged.

The baseball game got under way. The Dolphins were the visiting team. The other team, the Cardinals, jogged out to take their positions on the field.

A kid in the bleachers dropped his soda can. It hit the ground and spilled, and the kid started to cry. An old station wagon filled with teenagers cruised by, its radio blaring, its horn honking.

"Where do you put the film in?" Shari asked impatiently.

Greg stepped closer to help her examine it. "Here, I think," he said, pointing. "Doesn't the back come off?"

Shari fiddled with it. "No, I don't think so. Most of these automatic-developing cameras load in the front."

She pulled at the back, but the camera wouldn't open. She tried pulling off the bottom. No better luck. Turning the camera, she tried pulling off the lens. It wouldn't budge.

Greg took the camera from her. "There's no slot or opening in the front."

"Well, what kind of camera is it, anyway?" Shari demanded.

"Uh . . . let's see." Greg studied the front, examined the top of the lens, then turned the camera over and studied the back.

He stared up at her with a surprised look on his face. "There's no brand name. Nothing."

"How can a camera not have a name?" Shari shouted in exasperation. She snatched the camera away from him and examined it closely, squinting her eyes against the bright afternoon sunshine.

Finally, she handed the camera back to him, defeated. "You're right, Greg. No name. No words of any kind. Nothing. What a stupid camera," she added angrily.

"Whoa. Hold on," Greg told her. "It's not my camera, remember? I didn't buy it. I took it from the Coffman house."

"Well, let's at least figure out how to open it up and look inside," Shari said.

The first Dolphin batter popped up to the second baseman. The second batter struck out on three straight swings. The dozen or so spectators shouted encouragement to their team.

The little kid who had dropped his soda continued to cry. Three kids rode by on bikes, waving to friends on the teams, but not stopping to watch.

"I've tried and tried, but I can't figure out how to open it," Greg admitted.

"Give me it," Shari said and grabbed the camera away from him. "There has to be a button or something. There has to be some way of opening it. This is ridiculous."

When she couldn't find a button or lever of any kind, she tried pulling the back off once again, prying it with her fingernails. Then she tried turning the lens, but it wouldn't turn.

"I'm not giving up," she said, gritting her teeth. "I'm not. This camera has to open. It *has* to!"

"Give up. You're going to wreck it," Greg warned, reaching for it.

"Wreck it? How could I wreck it?" Shari demanded. "It has no moving parts. Nothing!"

"This is impossible," Greg said.

Making a disgusted face, she handed the camera to him. "Okay, I give up. Check it out yourself, Greg."

He took the camera, started to raise it to his face, then stopped.

Uttering a low cry of surprise, his mouth dropped open and his eyes gaped straight ahead. Startled, Shari turned to follow his shocked gaze.

"Oh *no!*"

There on the ground a few yards outside the first base line, lay Bird. He was sprawled on his back, his neck bent at an odd and unnatural angle, his eyes shut tight.

13

"Bird!" Shari cried.

Greg's breath caught in his throat. He felt as if he were choking. "Oh!" he finally managed to cry out in a shrill, raspy voice.

Bird didn't move.

Shari and Greg, running side by side at full speed, reached him together.

"Bird?" Shari knelt down beside him. "Bird?"

Bird opened one eye. "Gotcha," he said quietly. The weird half-smile formed on his face, and he exploded in high-pitched laughter.

It took Shari and Greg a while to react. They both stood open-mouthed, gaping at their laughing friend.

Then, his heart beginning to slow to normal, Greg reached down, grabbed Bird with both hands, and pulled him roughly to his feet.

"I'll hold him while you hit him," Greg offered, holding Bird from behind.

"Hey, wait — " Bird protested, struggling to squirm out of Greg's grasp.

"Good plan," Shari said, grinning.

"Ow! Hey — let go! Come on! Let go!" Bird protested, trying unsuccessfully to wrestle free. "Come on! What's your problem? It was a joke, guys."

"Very funny," Shari said, giving Bird a playful punch on the shoulder. "You're a riot, Bird."

Bird finally freed himself with a hard tug and danced away from both of them. "I just wanted to show you how bogus it is to get all worked up about that dumb camera."

"But, Bird — " Greg started.

"It's just broken, that's all," Bird said, brushing blades of recently cut grass off his uniform pants. "You think because it showed Michael falling down those stairs, there's something strange with it. But that's dumb. Real dumb."

"I know it," Greg replied sharply. "But how do you explain it?"

"I told you, man. It's wrecked. Broken. That's it."

"Bird — get over here!" a voice called, and Bird's fielder's glove came flying at his head. He caught it, waved with a grin to Shari and Greg, and jogged to the outfield along with the other members of the Dolphins.

Carrying the camera tightly in one hand, Greg

led the way to the bleachers. He and Shari sat down on the end of the bottom bench.

Some of the spectators had lost interest in the game already and had left. A few kids had taken a baseball off the field and were having their own game of catch behind the bleachers. Across the playground, four or five kids were getting a game of kickball started.

"Bird is such a dork," Greg said, his eyes on the game.

"He scared me to death," Shari exclaimed. "I really thought he was hurt."

"What a clown," Greg muttered.

They watched the game in silence for a while. It wasn't terribly interesting. The Dolphins were losing 12–3 going into the third inning. None of the players were very good.

Greg laughed as a Cardinal batter, a kid from their class named Joe Garden, slugged a ball that sailed out to the field and right over Bird's head.

"That's the third ball that flew over his head!" Greg cried.

"Guess he lost it in the sun!" Shari exclaimed, joining in the laughter.

They both watched Bird's long legs storking after the ball. By the time he managed to catch up with it and heave it towards the diamond, Joe Garden had already rounded the bases and scored.

There were loud *boos* from the bleachers.

The next Cardinal batter stepped to the plate. A few more kids climbed down from the bleachers, having seen enough.

"It's so hot here in the sun," Shari said, shielding her eyes with one hand. "And I've got lots of homework. Want to leave?"

"I just want to see the next inning," Greg said, watching the batter swing and miss. "Bird is coming up next inning. I want to stay and *boo* him."

"What are friends for?" Shari said sarcastically.

It took a long while for the Dolphins to get the third out. The Cardinals batted around their entire order.

Greg's T-shirt was drenched with sweat by the time Bird came to the plate in the top of the fourth.

Despite the loud *booing* from Shari and Greg, Bird managed to punch the ball past the shortstop for a single.

"Lucky hit!" Greg yelled, cupping his hands into a megaphone.

Bird pretended not to hear him. He tossed away his batter's helmet, adjusted his cap, and took a short lead off first base.

The next batter swung at the first pitch and fouled it off.

"Let's go," Shari urged, pulling Greg's arm. "It's too hot. I'm dying of thirst."

"Let's just see if Bird — "

Greg didn't finish his sentence.

The batter hit the next ball hard. It made a loud *thunk* as it left the bat.

A dozen people — players and spectators — cried out as the ball flew across the diamond, a sharp line drive, and slammed into the side of Bird's head with another *thunk*.

Greg watched in horror as the ball bounced off Bird and dribbled away onto the infield grass. Bird's eyes went wide with disbelief, confusion.

He stood frozen in place on the base path for a long moment.

Then both of his hands shot up above his head, and he uttered a shrill cry, long and loud, like the high-pitched whinny of a horse.

His eyes rolled up in his head. He sank to his knees. Uttered another cry, softer this time. Then collapsed, sprawling onto his back, his neck at an unnatural angle, his eyes closed.

He didn't move.

14

In seconds, the two coaches and both teams were running out to the fallen player, huddling over him, forming a tight, hushed circle around him.

Crying, "Bird! Bird!" Shari leapt off the bleachers and began running to the circle of horrified onlookers.

Greg started to follow, but stopped when he saw a familiar figure crossing the street at a full run, waving to him.

"Terry!" Greg cried.

Why was his brother coming to the playground? Why wasn't he at his after-school job at the Dairy Freeze?

"Terry? What's happening?" Greg cried.

Terry stopped, gasping for breath, sweat pouring down his bright red forehead. "I . . . ran . . . all . . . the . . . way," he managed to utter.

"Terry, what's wrong?" A sick feeling crept up from Greg's stomach.

As Terry approached, his face held the same

frightened expression as in the photograph Greg had snapped of him.

The same frightened expression. With the same house behind him across the street.

The snapshot had come true. Just as the snapshot of Bird lying on the ground had come true.

Greg's throat suddenly felt as dry as cotton. He realized that his knees were trembling.

"Terry, what *is* it?" he managed to cry.

"It's Dad," Terry said, putting a heavy hand on Greg's shoulder.

"Huh? Dad?"

"You've got to come home, Greg. Dad — he's been in a bad accident."

"An accident?" Greg's head spun. Terry's words weren't making any sense to him.

"In the new car," Terry explained, again placing a heavy hand on Greg's trembling shoulder. "The new car is totaled. Completely totaled."

"Oh," Greg gasped, feeling weak.

Terry squeezed his shoulder. "Come on. Hurry."

Holding the camera tightly in one hand, Greg began running after his brother.

Reaching the street, he turned back to the playground to see what was happening with Bird.

A large crowd was still huddled around Bird, blocking him from sight.

But — what was that dark shadow behind the bleachers? Greg wondered.

Someone — someone all in black — was hiding back there.

Watching Greg?

"Come *on!*" Terry urged.

Greg stared hard at the bleachers. The dark figure pulled back out of sight.

"Come *on,* Greg!"

"I'm coming!" Greg shouted, and followed his brother toward home.

15

The hospital walls were pale green. The uniforms worn by the nurses scurrying through the brightly lit corridors were white. The floor tiles beneath Greg's feet as he hurried with his brother towards their father's room were dark brown with orange specks.

Colors.

All Greg could see were blurs of colors, indistinct shapes.

His sneakers thudded noisily against the hard tile floor. He could barely hear them over the pounding of his heart.

Totaled. The car had been totaled.

Just like in the snapshot.

Greg and Terry turned a corner. The walls in this corridor were pale yellow. Terry's cheeks were red. Two doctors passed by wearing lime-green surgical gowns.

Colors. Only colors.

Greg blinked, tried to see clearly. But it was

61

all passing by too fast, all too unreal. Even the sharp hospital smell, that unique aroma of rubbing alcohol, stale food, and disinfectant, couldn't make it real for him.

Then the two brothers entered their father's room, and it all became real.

The colors faded. The images became sharp and clear.

Their mother jumped up from the folding chair beside the bed. "Hi, boys." She clenched a wadded-up tissue in her hand. It was obvious that she had been crying. She forced a tight smile on her face, but her eyes were red-rimmed, her cheeks pale and puffy.

Stopping just inside the doorway of the small room, Greg returned his mother's greeting in a soft, choked voice. Then his eyes, focusing clearly now, turned to his father.

Mr. Banks had a mummylike bandage covering his hair. One arm was in a cast. The other lay at his side and had a tube attached just below the wrist, dripping a dark liquid into the arm. The bedsheet was pulled up to his chest.

"Hey — how's it going, guys?" their father asked. His voice sounded fogged in, as if coming from far away.

"Dad — " Terry started.

"He's going to be okay," Mrs. Banks interrupted, seeing the frightened looks on her sons' faces.

"I feel great," Mr. Banks said groggily.

"You don't *look* so great," Greg blurted out, stepping up cautiously to the bed.

"I'm okay. Really," their father insisted. "A few broken bones. That's it." He sighed, then winced from some pain. "I guess I'm lucky."

"You're very lucky," Mrs. Banks agreed quickly.

What's the lucky part? Greg wondered silently to himself. He couldn't take his eyes off the tube stuck into his father's arm.

Again, he thought of the snapshot of the car. It was up in his room at home, tucked into the secret compartment in his headboard.

The snapshot showing the car totaled, the driver's side caved in.

Should he tell them about it?

He couldn't decide.

Would they believe him if he *did* tell them?

"What'd you break, Dad?" Terry asked, sitting down on the radiator in front of the windowsill, shoving his hands into his jeans pockets.

"Your father broke his arm and a few ribs," Mrs. Banks answered quickly. "And he had a slight concussion. The doctors are watching him for internal injuries. But, so far, so good."

"I was lucky," Mr. Banks repeated. He smiled at Greg.

"Dad, I have to tell you about this photo I took," Greg said suddenly, speaking rapidly, his voice

63

trembling with nervousness. "I took a picture of the new car, and — "

"The car is completely wrecked," Mrs. Banks interrupted. Sitting on the edge of the folding chair, she rubbed her fingers, working her wedding ring round and around, something she always did when she was nervous. "I'm glad you boys didn't see it." Her voice caught in her throat. Then she added, "It's a miracle he wasn't hurt any worse."

"This photo — " Greg started again.

"Later," his mother said brusquely. "Okay?" She gave him a meaningful stare.

Greg felt his face grow hot.

This is *important*, he thought.

Then he decided they probably wouldn't believe him, anyway. Who would believe such a crazy story?

"Will we be able to get another new car?" Terry asked.

Mr. Banks nodded carefully. "I have to call the insurance company," he said.

"I'll call them when I get home," Mrs. Banks said. "You don't exactly have a hand free."

Everyone laughed at that, nervous laughter.

"I feel kind of sleepy," Mr. Banks said. His eyes were halfway closed, his voice muffled.

"It's the painkillers the doctors gave you," Mrs. Banks told him. She leaned forward and patted his hand. "Get some sleep. I'll come back in a few hours."

She stood up, still fiddling with her wedding band, and motioned with her head toward the door.

"Bye, Dad," Greg and Terry said in unison.

Their father muttered a reply. They followed their mother out the door.

"What *happened*?" Terry asked as they made their way past a nurses' station, then down the long, pale yellow corridor. "I mean, the accident."

"Some guy ran right through a red light," Mrs. Banks said, her red-rimmed eyes straight ahead. "He plowed right into your father's side of the car. Said his brakes weren't working." She shook her head, tears forming in the corners of her eyes. "I don't know," she said, sighing. "I just don't know what to say. Thank goodness he's going to be okay."

They turned into the green corridor, walking side by side. Several people were waiting patiently for the elevator at the far end of the hall.

Once again, Greg found himself thinking of the snapshots he had taken with the weird camera.

First Michael. Then Terry. Then Bird. Then his father.

All four photos had shown something terrible. Something terrible that hadn't happened yet.

And then all four photos had come true.

Greg felt a chill as the elevator doors opened and the small crowd of people moved forward to squeeze inside.

What was the truth about the camera? he wondered.

Does the camera *show* the future?

Or does it actually *cause* bad things to happen?

16

"Yeah. I know Bird's okay," Greg said into the phone receiver. "I saw him yesterday, remember? He was lucky. Real lucky. He didn't have a concussion or anything."

On the other end of the line — in the house next door — Shari agreed, then repeated her request.

"No, Shari. I really don't want to," Greg replied vehemently.

"Bring it," Shari demanded. "It's *my* birthday."

"I don't want to bring the camera. It's not a good idea. Really," Greg told her.

It was the next weekend. Saturday afternoon. Greg had been nearly out the door, on his way next door to Shari's birthday party, when the phone rang.

"Hi, Greg. Why aren't you on your way to my party?" Shari had asked when he'd run to pick up the receiver.

"Because I'm on the phone with you," Greg had replied dryly.

"Well, bring the camera, okay?"

Greg hadn't looked at the camera, hadn't removed it from its hiding place since his father's accident.

"I don't want to bring it," he insisted, despite Shari's high-pitched demands. "Don't you understand, Shari? I don't want anyone else to get hurt."

"Oh, Greg," she said, talking to him as if he were a three-year-old. "You don't really believe that, do you? You don't really believe that camera can hurt people."

Greg was silent for a moment. "I don't know what I believe," he said finally. "I only know that first, Michael, then, Bird — "

Greg swallowed hard. "And I had a dream, Shari. Last night."

"Huh? What kind of dream?" Shari asked impatiently.

"It was about the camera. I was taking everyone's picture. My whole family — Mom, Dad, and Terry. They were barbecuing. In the back yard. I held up the camera. I kept saying, 'Say Cheese, Say Cheese,' over and over. And when I looked through the viewfinder, they were smiling back at me — but . . . they were skeletons. All of them. Their skin was gone, and — and . . ."

Greg's voice trailed off.

"What a dumb dream," Shari said, laughing.

"But that's why I don't want to bring the camera," Greg insisted. "I think — "

"Bring it, Greg," she interrupted. "It's not your camera, you know. All four of us were in the Coffman house. It belongs to all four of us. Bring it."

"But *why*, Shari?" Greg demanded.

"It'll be a goof, that's all. It takes such weird pictures."

"That's for sure," Greg muttered.

"We don't have anything else to do for my party," Shari told him. "I wanted to rent a video, but my mom says we have to go outdoors. She doesn't want her precious house messed up. So I thought we could take everyone's picture with the weird camera. You know. See what strange things come out."

"Shari, I really don't — "

"Bring it," she ordered. And hung up.

Greg stood for a long time staring at the phone receiver, thinking hard, trying to decide what to do.

Then he replaced the receiver and headed reluctantly up to his room.

With a loud sigh, he pulled the camera from its hiding place in his headboard. "It's Shari's birthday, after all," he said aloud to himself.

His hands were trembling as he picked it up. He realized he was afraid of it.

I shouldn't be doing this, he thought, feeling a heavy knot of dread in the pit of his stomach.

I know I shouldn't be doing this.

17

"How's it going, Bird?" Greg called, making his way across the flagstone patio to Shari's back yard.

"I'm feeling okay," Bird said, slapping his friend a high five. "The only problem is, ever since that ball hit me," Bird continued, frowning, "from time to time I start — *pluuccck cluuuck cluuuuck!* — clucking like a chicken!" He flapped his arms and started strutting across the back yard, clucking at the top of his voice.

"Hey, Bird — go lay an egg!" someone yelled, and everyone laughed.

"Bird's at it again," Michael said, shaking his head. He gave Greg a friendly punch on the shoulder. Michael, his red hair unbrushed as usual, was wearing faded jeans and a flowered Hawaiian sports shirt about three sizes too big for him.

"Where'd you get that shirt?" Greg asked, holding Michael at arm's length by the shoulders to admire it.

"In a cereal box," Bird chimed in, still flapping his arms.

"My grandmother gave it to me," Michael said, frowning.

"He made it in home ec," Bird interrupted. One joke was never enough.

"But why did you *wear* it?" Greg asked.

Michael shrugged. "Everything else was dirty."

Bird bent down, picked up a small clump of dirt from the lawn, and rubbed it on the back of Michael's shirt. "Now this one's dirty, too," he declared.

"Hey, you — " Michael reacted with playful anger, grabbing Bird and shoving him into the hedge.

"Did you bring it?"

Hearing Shari's voice, Greg turned towards the house and saw her jogging across the patio in his direction. Her black hair was pulled back in a single braid, and she had on an oversized, silky yellow top that came down over black spandex leggings.

"Did you bring it?" she repeated eagerly. A charm bracelet filled with tiny silver charms — a birthday present — jangled at her wrist.

"Yeah." Greg reluctantly held up the camera.

"Excellent," she declared.

"I really don't want — " Greg started.

"You can take my picture first since it's my birthday," Shari interrupted. "Here. How's this?"

She struck a sophisticated pose, leaning against a tree with her hand behind her head.

Greg obediently raised the camera. "Are you sure you want me to do this, Shari?"

"Yeah. Come on. I want to take everyone's picture."

"But it'll probably come out weird," Greg protested.

"I know," Shari replied impatiently, holding her pose. "That's the fun of it."

"But, Shari — "

"Michael puked on his shirt," he heard Bird telling someone near the hedge.

"I did not!" Michael was screaming.

"You mean it looks like that *naturally*?" Bird asked.

Greg could hear a lot of raucous laughing, all of it at Michael's expense.

"Will you take the picture!" Shari cried, holding on to the slender trunk of the tree.

Greg pointed the lens at her and pressed the button. The camera whirred, and the undeveloped, white square rolled out.

"Hey, are we the only boys invited?" Michael asked, stepping up to Shari.

"Yeah. Just you three," Shari said. "And nine girls."

"Oh, wow." Michael made a face.

"Take Michael's picture next," Shari told Greg.

"No way!" Michael replied quickly, raising his hands as if to shield himself and backing away. "The last time you took my picture with that thing, I fell down the stairs."

Trying to get away, Michael backed right into Nina Blake, one of Shari's friends. She reacted with a squeal of surprise, then gave him a playful shove, and he kept right on backing away.

"Michael, come on. It's *my* party," Shari called.

"What are we going to do? Is this *it*?" Nina demanded from halfway across the yard.

"I thought we'd take everyone's picture and then play a game or something," Shari told her.

"A game?" Bird chimed in. "You mean like Spin the Bottle?"

A few kids laughed.

"Truth or Dare!" Nina suggested.

"Yeah. Truth or Dare!" a couple of other girls called in agreement.

"Oh, no," Greg groaned quietly to himself. Truth or Dare meant a lot of kissing and awkward, embarrassing stunts.

Nine girls and only three boys.

It was going to be *really* embarrassing.

How could Shari *do* this to us? he wondered.

"Well, did it come out?" Shari asked, grabbing his arm. "Let me see."

Greg was so upset about having to play Truth or Dare, he had forgotten about the snapshot developing in his hand. He held it up, and they both examined it.

"Where am I?" Shari asked in surprise. "What were you aiming at? You missed me!"

"Huh?" Greg stared at the snapshot. There was the tree. But no Shari. "Weird! I pointed it right at you. I lined it up carefully," he protested.

"Well, you missed me. I'm not in the shot," Shari replied disgustedly.

"But, Shari — "

"I mean, come *on* — I'm not invisible, Greg. I'm not a vampire or something. I can see my reflection in mirrors. And I do usually show up in photos."

"But, look — " Greg stared hard at the photograph. "There's the tree you were leaning against. You can see the tree trunk clearly. And there's the spot where you were standing."

"But where *am* I?" Shari demanded, jangling her charm bracelet noisily. "Never mind." She grabbed the snapshot from him and tossed it on the grass. "Take another one. Quick."

"Well, okay. But — " Greg was still puzzling over the photo. Why hadn't Shari shown up in it? He bent down, picked it up, and shoved it into his pocket.

"Stand closer this time," she instructed.

Greg moved a few steps closer, carefully centered Shari in the viewfinder, and snapped the

74

picture. A square of film zipped out the front.

Shari walked over and pulled the picture from the camera. "This one better turn out," she said, staring hard at it as the colors began to darken and take form.

"If you really want pictures of everyone, we should get another camera," Greg said, his eyes also locked on the snapshot.

"Hey — I don't *believe* it!" Shari cried.

Again, she was invisible.

The tree photographed clearly, in perfect focus. But Shari was nowhere to be seen.

"You were right. The dumb camera is broken," she said disgustedly, handing the photo to Greg. "Forget it." She turned away from him and called to the others. "Hey, guys — Truth or Dare!"

There were some cheers and some groans.

Shari headed them back to the woods behind her back yard to play. "More privacy," she explained. There was a circular clearing just beyond the trees, a perfect, private place.

The game was just as embarrassing as Greg had imagined. Among the boys, only Bird seemed to be enjoying it. Bird loves dumb stuff like this, Greg thought, with some envy.

Luckily, after little more than half an hour, he heard Mrs. Walker, Shari's mom, calling from the house, summoning them back to cut the birthday cake.

"Aw, too bad," Greg said sarcastically. "Just when the game was getting good."

"We have to get out of the woods, anyway," Bird said, grinning. "Michael's shirt is scaring the squirrels."

Laughing and talking about the game, the kids made their way back to the patio where the pink-and-white birthday cake, candles all lit, was waiting on the round umbrella table.

"I must be a pretty bad mom," Mrs. Walker joked, "allowing you all to go off into the woods by yourselves."

Some of the girls laughed.

Cake knife in her hand, Mrs. Walker looked around. "Where's Shari?"

Everyone turned their eyes to search the back yard. "She was with us in the woods," Nina told Mrs. Walker. "Just a minute ago."

"Hey, Shari!" Bird called, cupping his hands to his mouth as a megaphone. "Earth calling Shari! It's cake time!"

No reply.

No sign of her.

"Did she go in the house?" Greg asked.

Mrs. Walker shook her head. "No. She didn't come by the patio. Is she still in the woods?"

"I'll go check," Bird told her. Calling Shari's name, he ran to the edge of the trees at the back of the yard. Then he disappeared into the trees, still calling.

A few minutes later, Bird emerged, signaling to the others with a shrug.

No sign of her.

They searched the house. The front yard. The woods again.

But Shari had vanished.

18

Greg sat in the shade with his back against the tree trunk, the camera on the ground at his side, and watched the blue-uniformed policemen.

They covered the back yard and could be seen bending low as they climbed around in the woods. He could hear their voices, but couldn't make out what they were saying. Their faces were intent, bewildered.

More policemen arrived, grim-faced, business-like.

And then, even more dark-uniformed police-men.

Mrs. Walker had called her husband home from a golf game. They sat huddled together on canvas chairs in a corner of the patio. They whispered to each other, their eyes darting across the yard. Holding hands, they looked pale and worried.

Everyone else had left.

On the patio, the table was still set. The birth-day candles had burned all the way down, the blue and red wax melting in hard puddles on the pink-and-white icing, the cake untouched.

"No sign of her," a red-cheeked policeman with a white-blond mustache was telling the Walkers. He pulled off his cap and scratched his head, revealing short, blond hair.

"Did someone . . . take her away?" Mr. Walker asked, still holding his wife's hand.

"No sign of a struggle," the policeman said. "No sign of anything, really."

Mrs. Walker sighed loudly and lowered her head. "I just don't understand it."

There was a long, painful silence.

"We'll keep looking," the policeman said. "I'm sure we'll find . . . something."

He turned and headed toward the woods.

"Oh. Hi." He stopped in front of Greg, staring down at him as if seeing him for the first time. "You still here, son? All the other guests have gone home." He pushed his hair back and replaced his cap.

"Yeah, I know," Greg replied solemnly, lifting the camera into his lap.

"I'm Officer Riddick," he said.

"Yeah, I know," Greg repeated softly.

"How come you didn't go home after we talked with you, like the others?" Riddick asked.

"I'm just upset, I guess," Greg told him. "I mean, Shari's a good friend, you know?" He cleared his throat, which felt dry and tight. "Be-

79

sides, I live right over there." He gestured with his head to his house next door.

"Well, you might as well go home, son," Riddick said, turning his eyes to the woods with a frown. "This search could take a long time. We haven't found a thing back there yet."

"I know," Greg replied, rubbing his hand against the back of the camera.

And I know that this camera is the reason Shari is missing, he thought, feeling miserable and frightened.

"One minute she was there. The next minute she was gone," the policeman said, studying Greg's face as if looking for answers there.

"Yeah," Greg replied. "It's so weird."

It's weirder than anyone knows, Greg thought.

The camera made her invisible. The camera did it.

First, she vanished from the snapshot.

Then she vanished in real life.

The camera did it to her. I don't know how. But it did.

"Do you have something more to tell me?" Riddick asked, hands resting on his hips, his right hand just above the worn brown holster that carried his pistol. "Did you see something? Something that might give us a clue, help us out? Something you didn't remember to tell me before?"

Should I tell him? Greg wondered.

If I tell him about the camera, he'll ask where I got it. And I'll have to tell him that I got it in the Coffman house. And we'll all get in trouble for breaking in there.

But — big deal. Shari is missing. Gone. Vanished. That's a lot more important.

I should tell him, Greg decided.

But then he hesitated. If I tell him, he won't believe me.

If I tell him, how will it help bring Shari back?

"You look very troubled," Riddick said, squatting down next to Greg in the shade. "What's your name again?"

"Greg. Greg Banks."

"Well, you look very troubled, Greg," the policeman repeated softly. "Why don't you tell me what's bothering you? Why don't you tell me what's on your mind? I think it'll make you feel a lot better."

Greg took a deep breath and glanced up to the patio. Mrs. Walker had covered her face with her hands. Her husband was leaning over her, trying to comfort her.

"Well . . ." Greg started.

"Go ahead, son," Riddick urged softly. "Do you know where Shari is?"

"It's this camera," Greg blurted out. He could suddenly feel the blood throbbing against his temples.

He took a deep breath and then continued. "You see, this camera is weird."

"What do you mean?" Riddick asked quietly.

Greg took another deep breath. "I took Shari's picture. Before. When I first arrived. I took two pictures. And she was invisible. In both of them. See?"

Riddick closed his eyes, then opened them. "No. I don't understand."

"Shari was invisible in the picture. Everything else was there. But she wasn't. She had vanished, see. And, then, later, she vanished for real. The camera — it predicts the future, I guess. Or it makes bad things happen." Greg raised the camera, attempting to hand it to the policeman.

Riddick made no attempt to take it. He just stared hard at Greg, his eyes narrowing, his expression hardening.

Greg felt a sudden stab of fear.

Oh, no, he thought. Why is he looking at me like that?

What is he going to do?

19

Greg continued to hold the camera out to the policeman.

But Riddick quickly climbed to his feet. "The camera makes bad things happen?" His eyes burned into Greg's.

"Yes," Greg told him. "It isn't my camera, see? And every time I take a picture — "

"Son, that's enough," Riddick said gently. He reached down and rested a hand on Greg's trembling shoulder. "I think you're very upset, Greg," he said, his voice almost a whisper. "I don't blame you. This is very upsetting for everyone."

"But it's *true* — " Greg started to insist.

"I'm going to ask that officer over there," Riddick said, pointing, "to take you home now. And I'm going to have him tell your parents that you've been through a very frightening experience."

I *knew* he wouldn't believe me, Greg thought angrily.

How could I have been so stupid?

Now he thinks I'm some kind of a nut case.

Riddick called to a policeman at the side of the house near the hedge.

"No, that's okay," Greg said, quickly pulling himself up, cradling the camera in his hand. "I can make it home okay."

Riddick eyed him suspiciously. "You sure?"

"Yeah. I can walk by myself."

"If you have anything to tell me later," Riddick said, lowering his gaze to the camera, "just call the station, okay?"

"Okay," Greg replied, walking slowly towards the front of the house.

"Don't worry, Greg. We'll do our best," Riddick called after him. "We'll find her. Put the camera away and try to get some rest, okay?"

"Okay," Greg muttered.

He hurried past the Walkers, who were still huddled together under the umbrella on the patio.

Why was I so stupid? he asked himself as he walked home. Why did I expect that policeman to believe such a weird story?

I'm not even sure I believe it myself.

A few minutes later, he pulled open the back screen door and entered his kitchen. "Anybody home?"

No reply.

He headed through the back hall towards the living room. "Anyone home?"

No one.

Terry was at work. His mother must have been visiting his dad at the hospital.

Greg felt bad. He really didn't feel like being alone now. He really wanted to tell them about what had happened to Shari. He really wanted to talk to them.

Still cradling the camera, he climbed the stairs to his room.

He stopped in the doorway, blinked twice, then uttered a cry of horror.

His books were scattered all over the floor. The covers had been pulled off his bed. His desk drawers were all open, their contents strewn around the room. The desk lamp was on its side on the floor. All of his clothes had been pulled from the dresser and his closet and tossed everywhere.

Someone had been in Greg's room — and had turned it upside down!

20

Who would do this? Greg asked himself, staring in horror at his ransacked room.

Who would tear my room apart like this?

He realized that he knew the answer. He knew who would do it, who *had* done it.

Someone looking for the camera.

Someone desperate to get the camera back.

Spidey?

The creepy guy who dressed all in black was living in the Coffman house. Was he the owner of the camera?

Yes, Greg knew, Spidey had done it.

Spidey had been watching Greg, spying on Greg from behind the bleachers at the Little League game.

He knew that Greg had his camera. *And he knew where Greg lived.*

That thought was the most chilling of all.

He knew where Greg lived.

Greg turned away from the chaos in his room,

leaned against the wall of the hallway, and closed his eyes.

He pictured Spidey, the dark figure creeping along so evilly on his spindly legs. He pictured him inside the house, Greg's house. Inside Greg's room.

He was here, thought Greg. He pawed through all my things. He wrecked my room.

Greg stepped back into his room. He felt all mixed up. He felt like shouting angrily and crying for help all at once.

But he was all alone. No one to hear him. No one to help him.

What now? he wondered. What now?

Suddenly, leaning against the doorframe, staring at his ransacked room, he knew what he had to do.

21

"Hey, Bird, it's me."

Greg held the receiver in one hand and wiped the sweat off his forehead with the other. He'd never worked so hard — or so fast — in all his life.

"Did they find Shari?" Bird asked eagerly.

"I haven't heard. I don't think so," Greg said, his eyes surveying his room. Almost back to normal.

He had put everything back, cleaned and straightened. His parents would never guess.

"Listen, Bird, I'm not calling about that," Greg said, speaking rapidly into the phone. "Call Michael for me, okay? Meet me at the playground. By the baseball diamond."

"When? Now?" Bird asked, sounding confused.

"Yeah," Greg told him. "We have to meet. It's important."

"It's almost dinnertime," Bird protested. "I don't know if my parents — "

"It's important," Greg repeated impatiently. "I've got to see you guys. Okay?"

"Well . . . maybe I can sneak out for a few minutes," Bird said, lowering his voice. And then Greg heard him shout to his mother: "It's no one, Ma! I'm talking to no one!"

Boy, *that's* quick thinking! Greg thought sarcastically. He's a worse liar than I am!

And then he heard Bird call to his mom: "I *know* I'm on the phone. But I'm not talking to anyone. It's only Greg."

Thanks a lot, pal, Greg thought.

"I gotta go," Bird said.

"Get Michael, okay?" Greg urged.

"Yeah. Okay. See you." He hung up.

Greg replaced the receiver, then listened for his mother. Silence downstairs. She still wasn't home. She didn't know about Shari, Greg realized. He knew she and his dad were going to be very upset.

Very upset.

Almost as upset as he was.

Thinking about his missing friend, he went to his bedroom window and looked down on her yard next door. It was deserted now.

The policemen had all left. Shari's shaken parents must have gone inside.

A squirrel sat under the wide shade of the big tree, gnawing furiously at an acorn, another acorn at his feet.

89

In the corner of the window, Greg could see the birthday cake, still sitting forlornly on the deserted table, the places all set, the decorations still standing.

A birthday party for ghosts.

Greg shuddered.

"Shari is alive," he said aloud. "They'll find her. She's alive."

He knew what he had to do now.

Forcing himself away from the window, he hurried to meet his two friends.

22

"No way," Bird said heatedly, leaning against the bleacher bench. "Have you gone totally bananas?"

Swinging the camera by its cord, Greg turned hopefully to Michael. But Michael avoided Greg's stare. "I'm with Bird," he said, his eyes on the camera.

Since it was just about dinnertime, the playground was nearly deserted. A few little kids were on the swings at the other end. Two kids were riding their bikes round and around the soccer field.

"I thought maybe you guys would come with me," Greg said, disappointed. He kicked up a clump of grass with his sneaker. "I have to return this thing," he continued, raising the camera. "I know it's what I have to do. I have to put it back where I found it."

"No way," Bird repeated, shaking his head. "I'm not going back to the Coffman house. Once was enough."

"Chicken?" Greg asked angrily.

"Yeah," Bird quickly admitted.

"You don't have to take it back," Michael argued. He pulled himself up the side of the bleachers, climbed onto the third deck of seats, then lowered himself to the ground.

"What do you mean?" Greg asked impatiently, kicking at the grass.

"Just toss it, Greg," Michael urged, making a throwing motion with one hand. "Heave it. Throw it in the trash somewhere."

"Yeah. Or leave it right here," Bird suggested. He reached for the camera. "Give it to me. I'll hide it under the seats."

"You don't understand," Greg said, swinging the camera out of Bird's reach. "Throwing it away won't do any good."

"Why not?" Bird asked, making another swipe for the camera.

"Spidey'll just come back for it," Greg told him heatedly. "He'll come back to my room looking for it. He'll come after me. I know it."

"But what if we get caught taking it back?" Michael asked.

"Yeah. What if Spidey's there in the Coffman house, and he catches us?" Bird said.

"You don't understand," Greg cried. "He knows where I live! He was in my house. He was in my *room*! He wants his camera back, and — "

"Here. Give it to me," Bird said. "We don't have

to go back to that house. He can find it. Right here."

He grabbed again for the camera.

Greg held tightly to the strap and tried to tug it away.

But Bird grabbed the side of the camera.

"No!" Greg cried out as it flashed. And whirred.

A square of film slid out.

"No!" Greg cried to Bird, horrified, staring at the white square as it started to develop. "You took *my* picture!"

His hand trembling, he pulled the snapshot from the camera.

What would it show?

23

"Sorry," Bird said. "I didn't mean to — "

Before he could finish his sentence, a voice interrupted from behind the bleachers. "Hey — what've you got there?"

Greg looked up from the developing snapshot in surprise. Two tough-looking boys stepped out of the shadows, their expressions hard, their eyes on the camera.

He recognized them immediately — Joey Ferris and Mickey Ward — two ninth-graders who hung out together, always swaggering around, acting tough, picking on kids younger than them.

Their specialty was taking kids' bikes, riding off on them, and dumping them somewhere. There was a rumor around school that Mickey had once beaten up a kid so badly that the kid was crippled for life. But Greg believed Mickey made up that rumor and spread it himself.

Both boys were big for their age. Neither of them did very well in school. And even though

94

they were always stealing bikes and skateboards, and terrorizing little kids, and getting into fights, neither of them ever seemed to get into serious trouble.

Joey had short blond hair, slicked straight up, and wore a diamondlike stud in one ear. Mickey had a round, red face full of pimples, stringy black hair down to his shoulders, and was working a toothpick between his teeth. Both boys were wearing heavy metal T-shirts and jeans.

"Hey, I've gotta get home," Bird said quickly, half-stepping, half-dancing away from the bleachers.

"Me, too," Michael said, unable to keep the fear from showing on his face.

Greg tucked the snapshot into his jeans pocket.

"Hey, you found my camera," Joey said, grabbing it out of Greg's hand. His small, gray eyes burned into Greg's as if searching for a reaction. "Thanks, man."

"Give it back, Joey," Greg said with a sigh.

"Yeah. Don't take that camera," Mickey told his friend, a smile spreading over his round face. "It's *mine!*" He wrestled the camera away from Joey.

"Give it back," Greg insisted angrily, reaching out his hand. Then he softened his tone. "Come on, guys. It isn't mine."

"I *know* it isn't yours," Mickey said, grinning. "Because it's *mine!*"

95

"I have to give it back to the owner," Greg told him, trying not to whine, but hearing his voice edge up.

"No, you don't. I'm the owner now," Mickey insisted.

"Haven't you ever heard of finders keepers?" Joey asked, leaning over Greg menacingly. He was about six inches taller than Greg, and a lot more muscular.

"Hey, let him have the thing," Michael whispered in Greg's ear. "You wanted to get rid of it — right?"

"No!" Greg protested.

"What's your problem, Freckle Face?" Joey asked Michael, eyeing Michael up and down.

"No problem," Michael said meekly.

"Hey — say cheese!" Mickey aimed the camera at Joey.

"Don't do it," Bird interrupted, waving his hands frantically.

"Why not?" Joey demanded.

"Because your face will break the camera," Bird said, laughing.

"You're real funny," Joey said sarcastically, narrowing his eyes threateningly, hardening his features. "You want that stupid smile to be permanent?" He raised a big fist.

"I know this kid," Mickey told Joey, pointing at Bird. "Thinks he's hot stuff."

Both boys stared hard at Bird, trying to scare him.

Bird swallowed hard. He took a step back, bumping into the bleachers. "No, I don't," he said softly. "I don't think I'm hot stuff."

"He looks like something I stepped in yesterday," Joey said.

He and Mickey cracked up, laughing high-pitched hyena laughs and slapping each other high fives.

"Listen, guys. I really need the camera back," Greg said, reaching out a hand to take it. "It isn't any good, anyway. It's broken. And it doesn't belong to me."

"Yeah, that's right. It's broken," Michael added, nodding his head.

"Yeah. Right," Mickey said sarcastically. "Let's just see." He raised the camera again and pointed it at Joey.

"Really, guys. I need it back," Greg said desperately.

If they took a picture with the camera, Greg realized, they might discover its secret. That its snapshots showed the future, showed only bad things happening to people. That the camera was evil. Maybe it even *caused* evil.

"Say cheese," Mickey instructed Joey.

"Just snap the stupid thing!" Joey replied impatiently.

No, Greg thought. I can't let this happen. I've got to return the camera to the Coffman house, to Spidey.

Impulsively, Greg leapt forward. With a cry, he snatched the camera away from Mickey's face.

"Hey — " Mickey reacted in surprise.

"Let's *go*!" Greg shouted to Bird and Michael.

And without another word, the three friends turned and began running across the deserted playground towards their homes.

His heart thudding in his chest, Greg gripped the camera tightly and ran as fast as he could, his sneakers pounding over the dry grass.

They're going to catch us, Greg thought, panting loudly now as he raced toward the street. They're going to catch us and pound us. They're going to take back the camera. We're dead meat. Dead meat.

Greg and his friends didn't turn around until they were across the street. Breathing noisily, they looked back — and cried out in relieved surprise.

Joey and Mickey hadn't budged from beside the bleachers. They hadn't chased after them. They were leaning against the bleachers, laughing.

"Catch you later, guys!" Joey called after them.

"Yeah. Later," Mickey repeated.

They both burst out laughing again, as if they had said something hilarious.

"That was close," Michael said, still breathing hard.

"They mean it," Bird said, looking very troubled. "They'll catch us later. We're history."

"Tough talk. They're just a lot of hot air," Greg insisted.

"Oh, yeah?" Michael cried. "Then why did we run like that?"

"Because we're late for dinner," Bird joked. "See you guys. I'm gonna catch it if I don't hurry."

"But the camera — " Greg protested, still gripping it tightly in one hand.

"It's too late," Michael said, nervously raking a hand back through his red hair.

"Yeah. We'll have to do it tomorrow or something," Bird agreed.

"Then you guys will come with me?" Greg asked eagerly.

"Uh . . . I've gotta go," Bird said without answering.

"Me, too," Michael said quickly, avoiding Greg's stare.

All three of them turned their eyes back to the playground. Joey and Mickey had disappeared. Probably off to terrorize some other kids.

"Later," Bird said, slapping Greg on the shoulder as he headed away. The three friends split up, running in different directions across lawns and driveways, heading home.

Greg had run all the way to his front yard before he remembered the snapshot he had shoved into his jeans pocket.

He stopped in the driveway and pulled it out.

The sun was lowering behind the garage. He held the snapshot up close to his face to see it clearly.

"Oh, no!" he cried. "I don't believe it!"

24

"This is *impossible!*" Greg cried aloud, gaping at the snapshot in his trembling hand.

How had Shari gotten into the photo?

It had been taken a few minutes before, in front of the bleachers on the playground.

But there was Shari, standing close beside Greg.

His hand trembling, his mouth hanging open in disbelief, Greg goggled at the photo.

It was very clear, very sharp. There they were on the playground. He could see the baseball diamond in the background.

And there they were. Greg and Shari.

Shari standing so clear, so sharp — right next to him.

And they were both staring straight ahead, their eyes wide, their mouths open, their expressions frozen in horror as a large shadow covered them both.

"Shari?" Greg cried, lowering the snapshot and

darting his eyes over the front yard. "Are you here? Can you hear me?"

He listened.

Silence.

He tried again.

"Shari? Are you here?"

"Greg!" a voice called.

Uttering a startled cry, Greg spun around. "Huh?"

"Greg!" the voice repeated. It took him a while to realize that it was his mother, calling to him from the front door.

"Oh. Hi, Mom." Feeling dazed, he slid the snapshot back into his jeans pocket.

"Where've you been?" his mother asked as he made his way to the door. "I heard about Shari. I've been so upset. I didn't know where you were."

"Sorry, Mom," Greg said, kissing her on the cheek. "I — I should've left a note."

He stepped into the house, feeling strange and out-of-sorts, sad and confused and frightened, all at the same time.

Two days later, on a day of high, gray clouds, the air hot and smoggy, Greg paced back and forth in his room after school.

The house was empty except for him. Terry had gone off a few hours before to his after-school job at the Dairy Freeze. Mrs. Banks had driven to the hospital to pick up Greg's dad, who was finally coming home.

Greg knew he should be happy about his dad's return. But there were still too many things troubling him, tugging at his mind.

Frightening him.

For one thing, Shari still hadn't been found.

The police were completely baffled. Their new theory was that she'd been kidnapped.

Her frantic, grieving parents waited home by the phone. But no kidnappers called to demand a ransom.

There were no clues of any kind.

Nothing to do but wait. And hope.

As the days passed, Greg felt more and more guilty. He was sure Shari hadn't been kidnapped. He knew that somehow, the camera had made her disappear.

But he couldn't tell anyone else what he believed.

No one would believe him. Anyone he tried to tell the story to would think he was crazy.

Cameras can't be evil, after all.

Cameras can't make people fall down stairs. Or crash their cars.

Or vanish from sight.

Cameras can only record what they see.

Greg stared out of his window, pressing his forehead against the glass, looking down on

Shari's back yard. "Shari — where *are* you?" he asked aloud, staring at the tree where she had posed.

The camera was still hidden in the secret compartment in his headboard. Neither Bird nor Michael would agree to help Greg return it to the Coffman house.

Besides, Greg had decided to hold on to it a while longer, in case he needed it as proof.

In case he decided to confide his fears about it to someone.

In case . . .

His other fear was that Spidey would come back, back to Greg's room, back for the camera.

So much to be frightened about.

He pushed himself away from the window. He had spent so much time in the past couple of days staring down at Shari's empty back yard.

Thinking. Thinking.

With a sigh, he reached into the headboard and pulled out two of the snapshots he had hidden in there along with the camera.

The two snapshots were the ones taken the past Saturday at Shari's birthday party. Holding one in each hand, Greg stared at them, hoping he could see something new, something he hadn't noticed before.

But the photos hadn't changed. They still showed her tree, her back yard, green in the sunlight. And no Shari. No one where Shari had been standing. As if the lens had penetrated right through her.

Staring at the photos, Greg let out a cry of anguish.

If only he had never gone into the Coffman house.

If only he had never stolen the camera.

If only he had never taken any photos with it.

If only . . . if only . . . if only . . .

Before he realized what he was doing, he was ripping the two snapshots into tiny pieces.

Panting loudly, his chest heaving, he tore at the snapshots and let the pieces fall to the floor.

When he had ripped them both into tiny shards of paper, he flung himself facedown on his bed and closed his eyes, waiting for his heart to stop pounding, waiting for the heavy feeling of guilt and horror to lift.

Two hours later, the phone by his bed rang.

It was Shari.

25

"Shari — is it really you?" Greg shouted into the phone.

"Yeah. It's me!" She sounded as surprised as he did.

"But how? I mean — " His mind was racing. He didn't know what to say.

"Your guess is as good as mine," Shari told him. And then she said, "Hold on a minute." And he heard her step away from the phone to talk to her mother. "Mom — stop crying already. Mom — it's really me. I'm home."

A few seconds later, she came back on the line. "I've been home for two hours, and Mom's still crying and carrying on."

"I feel like crying, too," Greg admitted. "I — I just can't believe it! Shari, where *were* you?"

The line was silent for a long moment. "I don't know," she answered finally.

"Huh?"

"I really don't. It was just so weird, Greg. One

minute, there I was at my birthday party. The next minute, I was standing in front of my house. And it was two days later. But I don't remember being away. Or being anywhere else. I don't remember anything at all."

"You don't remember going away? Or coming back?" Greg asked.

"No. Nothing," Shari said, her voice trembling.

"Shari, those pictures I took of you — remember? With the weird camera? You were invisible in them — "

"And then I disappeared," she said, finishing his thought.

"Shari, do you think — ?"

"I don't know," she replied quickly. "I — I have to get off now. The police are here. They want to question me. What am I going to tell them? They're going to think I had amnesia or flipped out or something."

"I — I don't know," Greg said, completely bewildered. "We have to talk. The camera — "

"I can't now," she told him. "Maybe tomorrow. Okay?" She called to her mother that she was coming. "Bye, Greg. See you." And then she hung up.

Greg replaced the receiver, but sat on the edge of his bed staring at the phone for a long time.

Shari was back.

She'd been back about two hours.

Two hours. Two hours. Two hours.

He turned his eyes to the clock radio beside the phone.

Just two hours before, he had ripped up the two snapshots of an invisible Shari.

His mind whirred with wild ideas, insane ideas.

Had he brought Shari back by ripping up the photos?

Did this mean that the camera *caused* her to disappear? That the camera *caused* all of the terrible things that showed up in its snapshots?

Greg stared at the phone for a long time, thinking hard.

He knew what he had to do. He had to talk to Shari. And he had to return the camera.

He met Shari on the playground the next afternoon. The sun floated high in a cloudless sky. Eight or nine kids were engaged in a noisy brawl of a soccer game, running one way, then the other across the outfield of the baseball diamond.

"Hey — you look like *you*!" Greg exclaimed as Shari came jogging up to where he stood beside the bleachers. He pinched her arm. "Yeah. It's you, okay."

She didn't smile. "I feel fine," she told him, rubbing her arm. "Just confused. And tired. The police asked me questions for hours. And when they finally went away, my parents started in."

"Sorry," Greg said quietly, staring down at his sneakers.

"I think Mom and Dad believe somehow it's my fault that I disappeared," Shari said, resting her back against the side of the bleachers, shaking her head.

"It's the camera's fault," Greg muttered. He raised his eyes to hers. "The camera is evil."

Shari shrugged. "Maybe. I don't know what to think. I really don't."

He showed her the snapshot, the one showing the two of them on the playground staring in horror as a shadow crept over them.

"How weird," Shari exclaimed, studying it hard.

"I want to take the camera back to the Coffman house," Greg said heatedly. "I can go home and get it now. Will you help me? Will you come with me?"

Shari started to reply, but stopped.

They both saw the dark shadow move, sliding toward them quickly, silently, over the grass.

And then they saw the man dressed all in black, his spindly legs pumping hard as he came at them.

Spidey!

Greg grabbed Shari's hand, frozen in fear.

He and Shari gaped in terror as Spidey's slithering shadow crept over them.

26

Greg had a shudder of recognition. He knew the snapshot had just come true.

As the dark figure of Spidey moved toward them like a black tarantula, Greg pulled Shari's hand. "Run!" he cried in a shrill voice he didn't recognize.

He didn't have to say it. They were both running now, gasping as they ran across the grass toward the street. Their sneakers thudded loudly on the ground as they reached the sidewalk and kept running.

Greg turned to see Spidey closing the gap. "He's catching up!" he managed to cry to Shari, who was a few steps ahead of him.

Spidey, his face still hidden in the shadows of his black baseball cap, moved with startling speed, his long legs kicking high as he pursued them.

"He's going to catch us!" Greg cried, feeling as

if his chest were about to burst. *"He's . . . too . . . fast!"*

Spidey moved even closer, his shadow scuttling over the grass.

Closer.

When the car horn honked, Greg screamed.

He and Shari stopped short.

The horn blasted out again.

Greg turned to see a familiar young man inside a small hatchback. It was Jerry Norman, who lived across the street. Jerry lowered his car window. "Is this man chasing you?" he asked excitedly. Without waiting for an answer, he backed the car towards Spidey. "I'm calling the cops, mister!"

Spidey didn't reply. Instead, he turned and darted across the street.

"I'm warning you — " Jerry called after him.

But Spidey had disappeared behind a tall hedge.

"Are you kids okay?" Greg's neighbor demanded.

"Yeah. Fine," Greg managed to reply, still breathing hard, his chest heaving.

"We're okay. Thanks, Jerry," Shari said.

"I've seen that guy around the neighborhood," the young man said, staring through the windshield at the tall hedge. "Never thought he was dangerous. You kids want me to call the police?"

"No. It's okay," Greg replied.

As soon as I give him back his camera, he'll stop chasing us, Greg thought.

"Well, be careful — okay?" Jerry said. "You need a lift home or anything?" He studied their faces as if trying to determine how frightened and upset they were.

Greg and Shari both shook their heads. "We'll be okay," Greg said. "Thanks."

Jerry warned them once again to be careful, then drove off, his tires squealing as he turned the corner.

"That was close," Shari said, her eyes on the hedge. "Why was Spidey chasing us?"

"He thought I had the camera. He wants it back," Greg told her. "Meet me tomorrow, okay? In front of the Coffman house. Help me put it back?"

Shari stared at him without replying, her expression thoughtful, wary.

"We're going to be in danger — all of us — until we put that camera back," Greg insisted.

"Okay," Shari said quietly. "Tomorrow."

27

Something scurried through the tall weeds of the unmowed front lawn. "What *was* that?" Shari cried, whispering even though no one else was in sight. "It was too big to be a squirrel."

She lingered behind Greg, who stopped to look up at the Coffman house. "Maybe it was a racoon or something," Greg told her. He gripped the camera tightly in both hands.

It was a little after three o'clock the next afternoon, a hazy, overcast day. Mountains of dark clouds threatening rain were rolling across the sky, stretching behind the house, casting it in shadow.

"It's going to storm," Shari said, staying close behind Greg. "Let's get this over with and go home."

"Good idea," he said, glancing up at the heavy sky.

Thunder rumbled in the distance, a low roar.

The old trees that dotted the front yard whispered and shook.

"We can't just run inside," Greg told her, watching the sky darken. "First we have to make sure Spidey isn't there."

Making their way quickly through the tall grass and weeds, they stopped at the living room window and peered in. Thunder rumbled, low and long, in the distance. Greg thought he saw another creature scuttle through the weeds around the corner of the house.

"It's too dark in there. I can't see a thing," Shari complained.

"Let's check out the basement," Greg suggested. "That's where Spidey hangs out, remember?"

The sky darkened to an eerie gray-green as they made their way to the back of the house and dropped to their knees to peer down through the basement windows at ground level.

Squinting through the dust-covered windowpanes they could see the makeshift, plywood table Spidey had made, the wardrobe against the wall, its doors still open, the colorful, old clothing spilling out, the empty frozen food boxes scattered on the floor.

"No sign of him," Greg whispered, cradling the camera in his arm as if it might try to escape from him if he didn't hold it tightly. "Let's get moving."

"Are — are you sure?" Shari stammered. She

wanted to be brave. But the thought that she had disappeared for two days — completely *vanished*, most likely because of the camera — that frightening thought lingered in her mind.

Michael and Bird were chicken, she thought. But maybe they were the smart ones.

She wished this were over. All over.

A few seconds later, Greg and Shari pushed open the front door. They stepped into the darkness of the front hall. And stopped.

And listened.

And then they both jumped at the sound of the loud, sudden crash directly behind them.

28

Shari was the first to regain her voice. "It's just the door!" she cried. "The wind — "

A gust of wind had made the front door slam.

"Let's get this over with," Greg whispered, badly shaken.

"We never should've broken into this house in the first place," Shari whispered as they made their way on tiptoe, step by creaking step, down the dark hallway toward the basement stairs.

"It's a little late for that," Greg replied sharply.

Pulling open the door to the basement steps, he stopped again. "What's that banging sound upstairs?"

Shari's features tightened in fear as she heard it, too, a repeated, almost rhythmic banging.

"Shutters?" Greg suggested.

"Yeah," she quickly agreed, breathing a sigh of relief. "A lot of the shutters are loose, remember?"

The entire house seemed to groan.

Thunder rumbled outside, closer now.

They stepped onto the landing, then waited for their eyes to adjust to the darkness.

"Couldn't we just leave the camera up here, and run?" Shari asked, more of a plea than a question.

"No. I want to put it back," Greg insisted.

"But, Greg — " She tugged at his arm as he started down the stairs.

"No!" He pulled out of her grasp. "He was in my *room*, Shari! He tore everything apart, looking for it. I want him to find it where it belongs. If he doesn't find it, he'll come back to my house. I *know* he will!"

"Okay, okay. Let's just hurry."

It was brighter in the basement, gray light seeping down from the four ground-level windows. Outside, the wind swirled and pushed against the windowpanes. A pale flash of lightning made shadows flicker against the basement wall. The old house groaned as if unhappy about the storm.

"What was *that*? Footsteps?" Shari stopped halfway across the basement and listened.

"It's just the house," Greg insisted. But his quivering voice revealed that he was as frightened as his companion, and he stopped to listen, too.

Bang. Bang. Bang.

The shutter high above them continued its rhythmic pounding.

"Where did you find the camera, anyway?" Shari whispered, following Greg to the far wall across from the enormous furnace with its cob-webbed ducts sprouting up like pale tree limbs.

"Over here," Greg told her. He stepped up to the worktable and reached for the vise clamped on the edge. "When I turned the vise, a door opened up. Some kind of hidden shelf. That's where the camera — "

He cranked the handle of the vise.

Once again, the door to the secret shelf popped open.

"Good," he whispered excitedly. He flashed Shari a smile.

He shoved the camera onto the shelf, tucking the carrying strap under it. Then he pushed the door closed. "We're out of here."

He felt so much better. So relieved. So much *lighter*.

The house groaned and creaked. Greg didn't care.

Another flash of lightning, brighter this time, like a camera flash, sent shadows flickering on the wall.

"Come on," he whispered. But Shari was already ahead of him, making her way carefully over the food cartons strewn everywhere, hurrying towards the steps.

They were halfway up the stairs, Greg one step behind Shari, when, above them, Spidey stepped silently into view on the landing, blocking their escape.

29

Greg blinked and shook his head, as if he could shake away the image of the figure that stared darkly down at him.

"No!" Shari cried out, and fell back against Greg.

He grabbed for the railing, forgetting that it had fallen under Michael's weight during their first unfortunate visit to the house. Luckily, Shari regained her balance before toppling them both down the stairs.

Lightning flashed behind them, sending a flash of white light across the stairway. But the unmoving figure on the landing above them remained shrouded in darkness.

"Let us go!" Greg finally managed to cry, finding his voice.

"Yeah. We returned your camera!" Shari added, sounding shrill and frightened.

Spidey didn't reply. Instead, he took a step towards them, onto the first step. And then he descended another step.

Nearly stumbling again, Greg and Shari backed down to the basement floor.

The wooden stairs squeaked in protest as the dark figure stepped slowly, steadily, down. As he reached the basement floor, a crackling bolt of lightning cast a blue light over him, and Greg and Shari saw his face for the first time.

In the brief flash of color, they saw that he was old, older than they had imagined. That his eyes were small and round like dark marbles. That his mouth was small, too, pursed in a tight, menacing grimace.

"We returned the camera," Shari said, staring in fear as Spidey crept closer. "Can't we go now? Please?"

"Let me see," Spidey said. His voice was younger than his face, warmer than his eyes. "Come."

They hesitated. But he gave them no choice.

Ushering them back across the cluttered floor to the worktable, he wrapped his large, spidery hand over the vise and turned the handle. The door opened. He pulled out the camera and held it close to his face to examine it.

"You shouldn't have taken it," he told them, speaking softly, turning the camera in his hands.

"We're sorry," Shari said quickly.

"Can we go now?" Greg asked, edging towards the stairs.

"It's not an ordinary camera," Spidey said, raising his small eyes to them.

"We know," Greg blurted out. "The pictures it took. They — "

Spidey's eyes grew wide, his expression angry. "You took pictures with it?"

"Just a few," Greg told him, wishing he had kept his mouth shut. "They didn't come out. Really."

"You know about the camera, then," Spidey said, moving quickly to the center of the floor.

Was he trying to block their escape? Greg wondered.

"It's broken or something," Greg said uncertainly, shoving his hands into his jeans pockets.

"It's not broken," the tall, dark figure said softly. "It's evil." He motioned toward the low plywood table. "Sit there."

Shari and Greg exchanged glances. Then, reluctantly, they sat down on the edge of the board, sitting stiffly, nervously, their eyes darting towards the stairway, towards escape.

"The camera is evil," Spidey repeated, standing over them, holding the camera in both hands. "I should know. I helped to create it."

"You're an inventor?" Greg asked, glancing at Shari, who was nervously tugging at a strand of her black hair.

"I'm a scientist," Spidey replied. "Or, I should say, I *was* a scientist. My name is Fredericks. Dr. Fritz Fredericks." He transferred the camera from one hand to the other. "My lab partner invented this camera. It was his pride and joy. More than that, it would have made him a fortune. *Would* have, I say." He paused, a thoughtful expression sinking over his face.

"What happened to him? Did he die?" Shari asked, still fiddling with the strand of hair.

Dr. Fredericks snickered. "No. Worse. I stole the invention from him. I stole the plans and the camera. I was evil, you see. I was young and greedy. So very greedy. And I wasn't above stealing to make my fortune."

He paused, eyeing them both as if waiting for them to say something, to offer their disapproval of him, perhaps. But when Greg and Shari remained silent, staring up at him from the low plywood table, he continued his story.

"When I stole the camera, it caught my partner by surprise. Unfortunately, from then on, all of the surprises were mine." A strange, sad smile twisted across his aged face. "My partner, you see, was much more evil than I was."

Dr. Fredericks coughed into his hand, then began to pace in front of Greg and Shari as he talked, speaking softly, slowly, as if remembering the story for the first time in a long while.

"My partner was a *true* evil one. He dabbled in

the dark arts. I should correct myself. He didn't just dabble. He was quite a master of it all."

He held up the camera, waving it above his head, then lowering it. "My partner put a curse on the camera. If he couldn't profit from it, he wanted to make sure that I never would, either. And so he put a curse on it."

He turned his gaze on Greg, leaning over him. "Do you know about how some primitive peoples fear the camera? They fear the camera because they believe that if it takes their picture, it will steal their soul." He patted the camera. "Well, this camera really *does* steal souls."

Staring up at the camera, Greg shuddered.

The camera had stolen Shari away.

Would it have stolen *all* of their souls?

"People have died because of this camera," Dr. Fredericks said, uttering a slow, sad sigh. "People close to me. That is how I came to learn of the curse, to learn of the camera's evil. And then I learned something just as frightening — the camera cannot be destroyed."

He coughed, cleared his throat noisily, and began to pace in front of them again. "And so I vowed to keep the camera a secret. To keep it away from people so it cannot do its evil. I lost my job. My family. I lost everything because of it. But I am determined to keep the camera where it can do no harm."

He stopped pacing with his back towards them.

123

He stood silently, shoulders hunched, lost in thought.

Greg quickly climbed to his feet and motioned for Shari to do the same. "Well . . . uh . . . I guess it's good we returned it," he said hesitantly. "Sorry we caused so much trouble."

"Yeah, we're very sorry," Shari repeated sincerely. "Guess it's back in the right hands."

"Good-bye," Greg said, starting towards the steps. "It's getting late, and we — "

"No!" Dr. Fredericks shouted, startling them both. He moved quickly to block the way. "I'm afraid you can't go. You know too much."

30

"I can never let you leave," Dr. Fredericks said, his face flickering in the blue glow of a lightning flash. He crossed his bony arms in front of his black sweatshirt.

"But we won't tell anyone," Greg said, his voice rising until the words became a plea. "Really."

"Your secret is good with us," Shari insisted, her frightened eyes on Greg.

Dr. Fredericks stared at them menacingly, but didn't reply.

"You can trust us," Greg said, his voice quivering. He cast a frightened glance at Shari.

"Besides," Shari said, "even if we *did* tell anyone, who would believe us?"

"Enough talk," Dr. Fredericks snapped. "It won't do you any good. I've worked too long and too hard to keep the camera a secret."

A rush of wind pushed against the windows, sending up a low howl. The wind carried a drumroll of rain. The sky through the basement windows was as black as night.

"You — can't keep us here *forever!*" Shari cried, unable to keep the growing terror from her voice.

The rain pounded against the windows now, a steady downpour.

Dr. Fredericks drew himself up straight, seemed to grow taller. His tiny eyes burned into Shari's. "I'm so sorry," he said, his voice a whisper of regret. "So sorry. But I have no choice."

He took another step towards them.

Greg and Shari exchanged frightened glances. From where they stood, in front of the low plywood table in the center of the basement, the steps seemed a hundred miles away.

"Wh-what are you going to do?" Greg cried, shouting over a burst of thunder that rattled the basement windows.

"Please — !" Shari begged. "Don't — !"

Dr. Fredericks moved forward with surprising speed. Holding the camera in one hand, he grabbed Greg's shoulder with the other.

"No!" Greg screamed. "Let go!"

"Let go of him!" Shari screamed.

She suddenly realized that both of Dr. Frederick's hands were occupied.

This may be my only chance, she thought.

She took a deep breath and lunged forward.

Dr. Fredericks' eyes bulged, and he cried out

in surprise as Shari grabbed the camera with both hands and pulled it away from him. He made a frantic grab for the camera, and Greg burst free.

Before the desperate man could take another step, Shari raised the camera to her eye and pointed the lens at him.

"Please — no! Don't push the button!" the old man cried.

He lurched forward, his eyes wild, and grabbed the camera with both hands.

Greg stared in horror as Shari and Dr. Fredericks grappled, both holding onto the camera, each trying desperately to wrestle it away from the other.

FLASH!

The bright burst of light startled them all.

Shari grabbed the camera. "Run!" she screamed.

31

The basement became a whirring blur of grays and blacks as Greg hurtled himself towards the stairs.

He and Shari ran side by side, slipping over the food cartons, jumping over tin cans and empty bottles.

Rain thundered against the windows. The wind howled, pushing against the glass. They could hear Dr. Fredericks' anguished screams behind them.

"Did it take our picture or his?" Shari asked.

"I don't know. Just *hurry!*" Greg screamed.

The old man was howling like a wounded animal, his cries competing with the rain and wind pushing at the windows.

The stairs weren't that far away. But it seemed to take forever to reach them.

Forever.

Forever, Greg thought. Dr. Fredericks wanted to keep Shari and him down there *forever*.

Panting loudly, they both reached the dark stairway. A deafening clap of thunder made them stop and turn around.

"Huh?" Greg cried aloud.

To his shock, Dr. Fredericks hadn't chased after them.

And his anguished cries had stopped.

The basement was silent.

"What's going on?" Shari cried breathlessly.

Squinting back into the darkness, it took Greg a while to realize that the dark, rumpled form lying on the floor in front of the worktable was Dr. Fredericks.

"What happened?" Shari cried, her chest heaving as she struggled to catch her breath. Still clinging to the camera strap, she gaped in surprise at the old man's still body, sprawled on its back on the floor.

"I don't know," Greg replied in a breathless whisper.

Reluctantly, Greg started back towards Dr. Fredericks. Following close behind, Shari uttered a low cry of horror when she clearly saw the fallen man's face.

Eyes bulged out, the mouth open in a twisted O of terror, the face stared up at them. Frozen. Dead.

Dr. Fredericks was dead.

"What — *happened*?" Shari finally managed to say, swallowing hard, forcing herself to turn away from the ghastly, tortured face.

"I think he died of fright," Greg replied, squeezing her shoulder and not even realizing it.

"Huh? Fright?"

"He knew better than anyone what the camera could do," Greg said. "When you snapped his picture, I think . . . I think it scared him to *death*!"

"I only wanted to throw him off-guard," Shari cried. "I only wanted to give us a chance to escape. I didn't think — "

"The picture," Greg interrupted. "Let's see the picture."

Shari raised the camera. The photo was still half-inside the camera. Greg pulled it out with a trembling hand. He held it up so they could both see it.

"Wow," he exclaimed quietly. "Wow."

The photo showed Dr. Fredericks lying on the floor, his eyes bulging, his mouth frozen open in horror.

Dr. Fredericks' fright, Greg realized — the fright that had killed him — was there, frozen on film, frozen on his face.

The camera had claimed another victim. This time, forever.

"What do we do now?" Shari asked, staring down at the figure sprawled at their feet.

"First, I'm putting this camera back," Greg said, taking it from her and shoving it back on its shelf. He turned the vise handle, and the door to the secret compartment closed.

Greg breathed a sigh of relief. Hiding the dreadful camera away made him feel so much better.

"Now, let's go home and call the police," he said.

Two days later, a cool, bright day with a gentle breeze rustling the trees, the four friends stopped at the curb, leaning on their bikes, and stared up at the Coffman house. Even in bright sunlight, the old trees that surrounded the house covered it in shade.

"So you didn't tell the police about the camera?" Bird asked, staring up at the dark, empty front window.

"No. They wouldn't believe it," Greg told him. "Besides, the camera should stay locked up forever. *Forever!* I hope no one ever finds out about it."

"We told the police we ran into the house to get out of the rain," Shari added. "And we said we started to explore while we waited for the storm to blow over. And we found the body in the basement."

"What did Spidey die of?" Michael asked, gazing up at the house.

"The police said it was heart failure," Greg told him. "But we know the truth."

"Wow. I can't believe one old camera could do so much evil," Bird said.

"I believe it," Greg said quietly.

"Let's get out of here," Michael urged. He raised his sneakers to the pedals and started to roll away. "This place really creeps me out."

The other three followed, pedaling away in thoughtful silence.

They had turned the corner and were heading up the next block when two figures emerged from the back door of the Coffman house. Joey Ferris and Mickey Ward stepped over the weed-choked lawn onto the driveway.

"Those jerks aren't too bright," Joey told his companion. "They never even saw us the other day. Never saw us watching them through the basement window."

Mickey laughed. "Yeah. They're jerks."

"They couldn't hide this camera from *us*. No way, man," Joey said. He raised the camera and examined it.

"Take my picture," Mickey demanded. "Come on. Let's try it out."

"Yeah. Okay." Joey raised the viewfinder to his eye. "Say cheese."

A click. A flash. A whirring sound.

Joey pulled the snapshot from the camera, and both boys eagerly huddled around it, waiting to see what developed.

THE CURSE OF THE MUMMY'S TOMB

1

I saw the Great Pyramid and got thirsty.

Maybe it was all the sand. So dry and yellow, it seemed to stretch on forever. It even made the sky look dry.

I poked my mom in the side. "Mom, I'm really thirsty."

"Not now," she said. She had one hand up on her forehead, shielding her eyes from the bright sun as she stared up at the enormous pyramid.

Not now?

What does "not now" mean? I was thirsty. *Now!*

Someone bumped me from behind and apologized in a foreign language. I never dreamed when I saw the Great Pyramid there'd be so many other tourists. I guess half the people in the world decided to spend their Christmas vacation in Egypt this year.

"But, Mom — " I said. I didn't mean to whine. It was just that my throat was so dry. "I'm really thirsty."

"We can't get you a drink now," she answered, staring at the pyramid. "Stop acting like you're four. You're twelve, remember?"

"Twelve-year-olds get thirsty, too," I muttered. "All this sand in the air, it's making me gag."

"Look at the pyramid," she said, sounding a little irritated. "That's why we came here. We didn't come here to get a drink."

"But I'm *choking*!" I cried, gasping and holding my throat.

Okay, so I wasn't choking. I exaggerated a little, just trying to get her attention. But she pulled the brim of her straw hat down and continued to stare up at the pyramid, which shimmered in the heat.

I decided to try my dad. As usual, he was studying the handful of guidebooks he always carried everywhere. I don't think he'd even looked at the pyramid yet. He always misses everything because he always has his nose buried in a guidebook.

"Dad, I'm really thirsty," I said, whispering as if my throat were strained to get my message across.

"Wow. Do you know how wide the pyramid is?" he asked, staring at a picture of the pyramid in his book.

"I'm thirsty, Dad."

"It's thirteen acres wide, Gabe," he said, really

excited. "Do you know what it's made of?"

I wanted to say Silly Putty.

He's always testing me. Whenever we go on a trip, he always asks me a million questions like that. I don't think I've ever answered one right.

"Some kind of stone?" I answered.

"That's right." He smiled at me, then turned back to his book. "It's made of limestone. Limestone blocks. It says here that some of the blocks weigh up to a thousand tons."

"Whoa," I said. "That's more than you and Mom put together!"

He turned his eyes from the book and frowned at me. "Not funny, Gabe."

"Just kidding," I said. Dad's a little sensitive about his weight, so I try to tease him about it as often as I can.

"How do you think the ancient Egyptians moved stones that weighed a thousand tons?" he asked.

Quiz time wasn't over.

I took a guess. "In trucks?"

He laughed. "Trucks? They didn't have the *wheel*."

I shielded my eyes and stared up at the pyramid. It was really huge, much bigger than it looks in pictures. And much dryer.

I couldn't imagine how they pulled those big stones across the sand without wheels. "I don't know," I confessed. "I'm really thirsty."

"No one knows how they did it," Dad said.

So it was a trick question.

"Dad, I really need a drink."

"Not now," he said. He squinted at the pyramid. "Gives you a funny feeling, doesn't it?"

"It gives me a thirsty feeling," I said, trying to get my point across.

"No. I mean, it gives me a funny feeling to think that our ancestors — yours and mine, Gabe — may have walked around these pyramids, or even helped to build them. It gives me kind of a chill. How about you?"

"I guess," I told him. He was right. It *was* kind of exciting.

We're Egyptian, you see. I mean, both sets of my grandparents came from Egypt. They moved to the United States around 1930. My mom and dad were both born in Michigan. We were all very excited to see the country our ancestors came from.

"I wonder if your uncle Ben is down inside that pyramid right now," Dad said, shielding his eyes from the sun with one hand.

Uncle Ben Hassad. I had nearly forgotten about my uncle, the famous archaeologist. Uncle Ben was another one of the reasons we had decided to come to Egypt over the holidays. That and the fact that my mom and dad had some business to do in Cairo and Alexandria and some other places.

Mom and Dad have their own business. They sell refrigeration equipment. It usually isn't very exciting. But sometimes they travel to neat places, like Egypt, and I get to go with them.

I turned my eyes to the pyramids and thought about my uncle.

Uncle Ben and his workers were digging around in the Great Pyramid, exploring and discovering new mummies, I guess. He had always been fascinated by our ancestors' homeland. He had lived in Egypt for many years. Uncle Ben was an expert on pyramids and mummies. I even saw his picture once in *National Geographic*.

"When are we going to see Uncle Ben?" I asked, tugging Dad's arm. I accidentally tugged too hard, and the guidebooks fell out of his hands.

I helped him pick them up.

"Not today," Dad said, making a face. He didn't like to bend over to pick up things. His stomach got in the way. "Ben's going to meet us in Cairo in a few days."

"Why don't we go up to the pyramid and see if he's there now?" I asked impatiently.

"We're not allowed," Dad replied.

"Look — camels!" Mom poked me on the shoulder and pointed.

Sure enough, some people had arrived on camels. One of the camels seemed to be having a coughing fit. I guess he was thirsty, too. The people riding the camels were tourists and they looked very uncomfortable. They didn't seem to know what to do next.

"Do you know how to get down from a camel?" I asked my dad.

He was squinting at the pyramid, studying the top of it. "No. How?"

"You don't get down from a camel," I said. "You get down from a duck."

I know. I know. It's a very old joke. But my dad and I never get tired of it.

"Do you see the camels?" Mom asked.

"I'm not blind," I replied. Being thirsty always puts me in a bad mood. Besides, what was so exciting about camels? They were really gross-looking, and they smelled like my gym socks after a basketball game.

"What's your problem?" Mom asked, fiddling with her straw hat.

"I *told* you," I said, not meaning to sound so angry. "I'm thirsty."

"Gabe, really." She glanced at Dad, then went back to staring at the pyramid.

"Dad, do you think Uncle Ben can take us inside the pyramid?" I asked enthusiastically. "That would really be outstanding."

"No, I don't think so," he said. He tucked his guidebooks into his armpit so he could raise his binoculars to his eyes. "I really don't think so, Gabe. I don't think it's allowed."

140

I couldn't hide my disappointment. I had all these fantasies about going down into the pyramid with my uncle, discovering mummies and ancient treasures. Fighting off ancient Egyptians who had come back to life to defend their sacred tomb, and escaping after a wild chase, just like Indiana Jones.

"I'm afraid you'll just have to appreciate the pyramid from the outside," Dad said, peering over the yellow sand, trying to focus the binoculars.

"I've already appreciated it," I told him glumly. "Can we go get a drink now?"

Little did I know that in a few days, Mom and Dad would be gone, and I would be deep inside the pyramid we were staring at. Not just inside it, but *trapped* inside it, *sealed* inside it — probably forever.

2

We drove from al-Jizah back to Cairo in the funny little rental car Dad had picked up at the airport. It wasn't a long drive, but it seemed long to me. The car was just a little bit bigger than some of my old remote-control cars, and my head hit the ceiling with every bump.

I'd brought my Game Boy with me, but Mom made me put it away so that I could watch the Nile as the road followed along its bank. It was very wide and very brown.

"No one else in your class is seeing the Nile this Christmas," Mom said, the hot wind blowing her brown hair through the open car window.

"Can I play with my Game Boy now?" I asked.

I mean, when you get right down to it, a river is a river.

An hour or so later, we were back in Cairo with its narrow, crowded streets. Dad made a wrong turn and drove us into some kind of market, and we were trapped in a little alley behind a herd of goats for nearly half an hour.

I didn't get a drink till we got back to the hotel, and by that time, my tongue was the size of a salami and hanging down to the floor just like Elvis's. He's our cocker spaniel back home.

I'll say one nice thing about Egypt. The Coke tastes just as good as the Coke back home. It's the Classic Coke, too, not the other kind. And they give you plenty of ice, which I like to crunch with my teeth.

We had a suite at the hotel, two bedrooms and a sort of living room. If you looked out the window, you could see a tall, glass skyscraper across the street, just like you'd see in any city.

There was a TV in the living room, but everyone spoke Arabic on it. The shows didn't look too interesting, anyway. Mainly a lot of news. The only channel in English was CNN. But that was news, too.

We had just started to talk about where to go for dinner when the phone rang. Dad went into the bedroom to answer it. A few minutes later he called Mom in, and I could hear the two of them discussing something.

They were talking very quietly, so I figured it had something to do with me and they didn't want me to hear it.

As usual, I was right.

They both came out of the bedroom a few minutes later, looking kind of worried. My first thought was that my grandmother had called to say that something bad had happened to Elvis back home.

"What's wrong?" I asked. "Who called?"

"Your dad and I have to go to Alexandria. Right away," Mom said, sitting down beside me on the couch.

"Huh? Alexandria?" We weren't supposed to go there until the end of the week.

"Business," Dad said. "An important customer wants to meet with us first thing tomorrow morning."

"We have to take a plane that leaves in an hour," Mom said.

"But I don't *want* to," I told them, jumping up from the couch. "I want to stay in Cairo and see Uncle Ben. I want to go to the pyramids with him. You promised!"

We argued about it for a short while. They tried to convince me there were a lot of cool things to see in Alexandria, but I held my ground.

Finally, Mom had an idea. She went into the bedroom, and I heard her making a phone call to someone. A few minutes later, she came back with a smile on her face. "I talked to Uncle Ben," she announced.

"Wow! Do they have phones in the pyramid?" I asked.

"No. I talked to him at the small lodge he's staying at in al-Jizah," she replied. "He said he'd come and take care of you, if you want. While your dad and I are in Alexandria."

"Yeah?" This was starting to sound outstanding. Uncle Ben is one of the coolest guys I've ever known. Sometimes I couldn't believe he was Mom's brother.

"It's your choice, Gabe," she said, glancing at my dad. "You can come with us, or you can stay with Ben till we get back."

Some choice.

I didn't have to think about it for more than one-eighteenth of a second. "I'll stay with Uncle Ben!" I declared.

"One other thing," Mom said, grinning for some reason. "You might want to think about this."

"I don't care *what* it is," I insisted. "I choose Uncle Ben."

"Sari is also on Christmas vacation," Mom said. "And she's staying with him, too."

"Barf!" I cried, and I flung myself down on the couch and began pounding the cushions with both fists.

Sari is Uncle Ben's stuck-up daughter. My only cousin. She's the same age as me — twelve — and she thinks she's so great. She goes to boarding school in the United States while her dad works in Egypt.

She's really pretty, and she knows it. And she's smart. And the last time I saw her, she was an inch taller than me.

That was last Christmas, I guess. She thought she was really hot stuff because she could get to the last level of *Super Mario Land*. But it wasn't fair because I don't have Super Nintendo, only regular Nintendo. So I never get to practice.

I think that's what she liked about me best, that she could beat me at games and things. Sari is the most competitive person I know. She has to be first and best at everything. If everyone around is catching the flu, she has to be the *first* one to catch it!

"Stop pounding the couch like that," Mom said. She grabbed my arm and pulled me to my feet.

"Does that mean you changed your mind? You're coming with us?" Dad asked.

I thought about it. "No. I'll stay here with Uncle Ben," I decided.

"And you won't fight with Sari?" Mom asked.

"She fights with me," I said.

"Your mom and I have got to hurry," Dad said.

They disappeared into the bedroom to pack. I turned on the TV and watched some kind of game show in Arabic. The contestants kept laughing a lot. I couldn't figure out why. I hardly know a word of Arabic.

After a while, Mom and Dad came out again,

dragging suitcases. "We'll never get to the airport in time," Dad said.

"I talked to Ben," Mom told me, brushing her hair with her hand. "He'll be here in an hour, hour and a half. Gabe, you don't mind staying alone here for just an hour, do you?"

"Huh?"

Not much of an answer, I'll admit. But her question caught me by surprise.

I mean, it never occurred to me that my own parents would leave me all alone in a big hotel in a strange city where I didn't even know the language. I mean, how could they do that to me?

"No problem," I said. "I'll be fine. I'll just watch TV till he comes."

"Ben's on his way already," Mom said. "He and Sari will be here in no time. And I phoned down to the hotel manager. He said he'd have someone look in on you from time to time."

"Where's the bellhop?" Dad asked, nervously pacing to the door and back. "I called down there ten minutes ago."

"Just stay here and wait for Ben, okay?" Mom said to me, walking up behind the couch, leaning over, and squeezing my ears. For some reason, she thinks I like that. "Don't go out or anything. Just wait right here for him." She bent down and kissed me on the forehead.

"I won't move," I promised. "I'll stay right here

147

on the couch. I won't go to the bathroom or anything."

"Can't you ever be serious?" Mom asked, shaking her head.

There was a loud knock on the door. The bellhop, a bent-over old man who didn't look as if he could pick up a feather pillow, had arrived to take the bags.

Mom and Dad, looking very worried, gave me hugs and more final instructions, and told me once again to stay in the room. The door closed behind them, and it was suddenly very quiet.

Very quiet.

I turned up the TV just to make it a little noisier. The game show had gone off, and now a man in a white suit was reading the news in Arabic.

"I'm not scared," I said aloud. But I had kind of a tight feeling in my throat.

I walked to the window and looked out. The sun was nearly down. The shadow of the skyscraper slanted over the street and onto the hotel.

I picked up my Coke glass and took a sip. It was watery and flat. My stomach growled. I suddenly realized that I was hungry.

Room service, I thought.

Then I decided I'd better not. What if I called and they only spoke Arabic?

I glanced at the clock. Seven-twenty. I wished Uncle Ben would arrive.

I wasn't scared. I just wished he'd arrive.

Okay. Maybe I was a little nervous.

I paced back and forth for a bit. I tried playing *Tetris* on the Game Boy, but I couldn't concentrate, and the light wasn't very good.

Sari is probably a champ at *Tetris*, I thought bitterly. Where *were* they? What was taking so long?

I began to have horrible, frightening thoughts: What if they can't find the hotel? What if they get mixed up and go to the wrong hotel?

What if they're in a terrible car crash and die? And I'm all by myself in Cairo for days and days?

I know. They were dumb thoughts. But they're the kind of thoughts you have when you're alone in a strange place, waiting for someone to come.

I glanced down and realized I had taken the mummy hand out of my jeans pocket.

It was small, the size of a child's hand. A little hand wrapped in papery brown gauze. I had bought it at a garage sale a few years ago, and I always carried it around as a good luck charm.

The kid who sold it to me called it a "Summoner." He said it was used to summon evil spirits, or something. I didn't care about that. I just thought it was an outstanding bargain for two dollars. I mean, what a great thing to find at a garage sale! And maybe it was even real.

I tossed it from hand to hand as I paced the length of the living room. The TV was starting to make me nervous, so I clicked it off.

But now the quiet was making me nervous.

I slapped the mummy hand against my palm and kept pacing.

Where were they? They should've been here by now.

I was beginning to think that I'd made the wrong choice. Maybe I should've gone to Alexandria with Mom and Dad.

Then I heard a noise at the door. Footsteps.

Was it them?

I stopped in the middle of the living room and listened, staring past the narrow front hallway to the door.

The light was dim in the hallway, but I saw the doorknob turn.

That's strange, I thought. Uncle Ben would knock first — wouldn't he?

The doorknob turned. The door started to creak open.

"Hey — " I called out, but the word choked in my throat.

Uncle Ben would knock. He wouldn't just barge in.

Slowly, slowly, the door squeaked open as I stared, frozen in the middle of the room, unable to call out.

Standing in the doorway was a tall, shadowy figure.

I gasped as the figure lurched into the room,

and I saw it clearly. Even in the dim light, I could see what it was.

A mummy.

Glaring at me with round, dark eyes through holes in its ancient, thick bandages.

A mummy.

Pushing itself off the wall and staggering stiffly toward me into the living room, its arms outstretched as if to grab me.

I opened my mouth to scream, but no sound came out.

3

I took a step back, and then another. Without realizing it, I'd raised my little mummy hand in the air, as if trying to fend off the intruder with it.

As the mummy staggered into the light, I stared into its deep, dark eyes.

And recognized them.

"Uncle Ben!" I screamed.

Angrily, I heaved the mummy hand at him. It hit his bandaged chest and bounced off.

He collapsed backwards against the wall, laughing that booming laugh of his.

And then I saw Sari poking her head in the doorway. She was laughing, too.

They both thought it was hilarious. But my heart was pounding so hard, I thought it was going to pop out of my chest.

"That wasn't funny!" I shouted angrily, balling my hands into fists at my sides. I took a deep breath, then another, trying to get my breathing to return to normal.

"I told you he'd be scared," Sari said, walking into the room, a big, superior grin on her face.

Uncle Ben was laughing so hard, he had tears running down his bandaged face. He was a big man, tall and broad, and his laughter shook the room. "You weren't that scared — were you, Gabe?"

"I knew it was you," I said, my heart still pounding as if it were a windup toy someone had wound up too tight. "I recognized you right away."

"You sure *looked* scared," Sari insisted.

"I didn't want to spoil the joke," I replied, wondering if they could see how terrified I really was.

"You should've seen the look on your face!" Uncle Ben cried, and started laughing all over again.

"I told Daddy he shouldn't do it," Sari said, dropping down onto the couch. "I'm amazed the hotel people let him come up dressed like that."

Uncle Ben bent down and picked up the mummy hand I had tossed at him. "You're used to me and my practical jokes, right, Gabe?"

"Yeah," I said, avoiding his eyes.

Secretly, I scolded myself for falling for his stupid costume. I was always falling for his dumb jokes. Always. And, now, there was Sari grinning at me from the couch, knowing I was so scared that I'd practically had a cow.

Uncle Ben pulled some of the bandages away from his face. He stepped over and handed the little mummy hand back to me. "Where'd you get that?" he asked.

"Garage sale," I told him.

I started to ask him if it was real, but he surrounded me in a big bear hug. The gauze felt rough against my cheek. "Good to see you, Gabe," he said softly. "You've grown taller."

"Almost as tall as me," Sari chimed in.

Uncle Ben motioned to her. "Get up and help me pull this stuff off."

"I kind of like the way you look in it," Sari said.

"Get over here," Uncle Ben insisted.

Sari got up with a sigh, tossing her straight black hair behind her shoulders. She walked over to her dad and started unraveling the bandages.

"I got a little carried away with this mummy thing, Gabe," Uncle Ben admitted, resting his arm on my shoulder as Sari continued working. "But it's just because I'm so excited about what's going on at the pyramid."

"What's going on?" I asked eagerly.

"Daddy's discovered a whole new burial chamber," Sari broke in before her dad had a chance to tell me himself. "He's exploring parts of the pyramid that have been undiscovered for thousands of years."

"Really?" I cried. "That's outstanding!"

Uncle Ben chuckled. "Wait till you see it."

"See it?" I wasn't sure what he meant. "You mean you're going to take me into the pyramid?"

My voice was so high that only dogs could hear it. But I didn't care. I couldn't believe my good luck. I was actually going inside the Great Pyramid, into a section that hadn't been discovered until now.

"I have no choice," Uncle Ben said dryly. "What else am I going to do with you two?"

"Are there mummies in there?" I asked. "Will we see actual mummies?"

"Do you miss your mummy?" Sari said, her lame idea of a joke.

I ignored her. "Is there treasure down there, Uncle Ben? Egyptian relics? Are there wall paintings?"

"Let's talk about it at dinner," he said, tugging off the last of the bandages. He was wearing a plaid sportshirt and baggy chinos under all the gauze. "Come on. I'm starving."

"Race you downstairs," Sari said, and shoved me out of the way to give herself a good head start out of the room.

We ate downstairs in the hotel restaurant. There were palm trees painted on the walls, and miniature palm trees planted in big pots all around the restaurant. Large wooden ceiling fans whirled slowly overhead.

The three of us sat in a large booth, Sari and I

across from Uncle Ben. We studied the long menus. They were printed in Arabic and English.

"Listen to this, Gabe," Sari said, a smug smile on her face. She began to read the Arabic words aloud.

What a show-off.

The white-suited waiter brought a basket of flat pita bread and a bowl of green stuff to dip the bread in. I ordered a club sandwich and French fries. Sari ordered a hamburger.

Later, as we ate our dinner, Uncle Ben explained a little more about what he had discovered at the pyramid. "As you probably know," he started, tearing off a chunk of the flat bread, "the pyramid was built some time around 2500 B.C., during the reign of the Pharaoh Khufu."

"*Gesundheit,*" Sari said. Another lame joke.

Her father chuckled. I made a face at her.

"It was the biggest structure of its time," Uncle Ben said. "Do you know how wide the base of the pyramid is?"

Sari shook her head. "No. How wide?" she asked with a mouthful of hamburger.

"I know," I said, grinning. "It's thirteen acres wide."

"Hey — that's right!" Uncle Ben exclaimed, obviously impressed.

Sari flashed me a surprised look.

That's one for me! I thought happily, sticking my tongue out at her.

And one for my dad's guidebooks.

"The pyramid was built as a royal burial place," Uncle Ben continued, his expression turning serious. "The Pharaoh made it really enormous so that the burial chamber could be hidden. The Egyptians worried about tomb robbers. They knew that people would try to break in and take all of the valuable jewels and treasures that were buried alongside their owners. So they built dozens of tunnels and chambers inside, a confusing maze to keep robbers from finding the real burial room."

"Pass the ketchup, please," Sari interrupted. I passed her the ketchup.

"Sari's heard all this before," Uncle Ben said, dipping the pita bread into the dark gravy on his plate. "Anyway, we archaeologists thought we'd uncovered all of the tunnels and rooms inside this pyramid. But a few days ago, my workers and I discovered a tunnel that isn't on any of the charts. An unexplored, undiscovered tunnel. And we think this tunnel may lead us to the actual burial chamber of Khufu himself!"

"Outstanding!" I exclaimed. "And Sari and I will be there when you discover it?"

Uncle Ben chuckled. "I don't know about that, Gabe. It may take us years of careful exploration. But I'll take you down into the tunnel tomorrow. Then you can tell your friends you were actually inside the ancient pyramid of Khufu."

"I've already been in it," Sari bragged. She

turned her eyes to me. "It's very dark. You might get scared."

"No, I won't," I insisted. "No way."

The three of us spent the night in my parents' hotel room. It took me hours to get to sleep. I guess I was excited about going into the pyramid. I kept imagining that we found mummies and big chests of ancient jewels and treasure.

Uncle Ben woke us up early the next morning, and we drove out to the pyramid outside al-Jizah. The air was already hot and sticky. The sun seemed to hang low over the desert like an orange balloon.

"There it is!" Sari declared, pointing out the window. And I saw the Great Pyramid rising up from the yellow sand like some kind of mirage.

Uncle Ben showed a special permit to the blue-uniformed guard, and we followed a narrow, private road that curved through the sand behind the pyramid. We parked beside several other cars and vans in the blue-gray shadow of the pyramid.

As I stepped out of the car, my chest was thudding with excitement. I stared up at the enormous, worn stones of the Great Pyramid.

It's over four thousand years old, I thought. I'm about to go inside something that was built four thousand years ago!

"Your sneaker's untied," Sari said, pointing.

She sure knew how to bring a guy back down to earth.

I bent in the sand to tie my sneaker. For some reason, the left one was always coming untied, even when I double-knotted it.

"My workers are already inside," Uncle Ben told us. "Now, stick close together, okay? Don't wander off. The tunnels really are like a maze. It's very easy to get lost."

"No problem," I said, my trembling voice revealing how nervous and excited I was.

"Don't worry. I'll keep an eye on Gabe, Dad," Sari said.

She was only two months older than me. Why did she have to act like she was my baby-sitter or something?

Uncle Ben handed us both flashlights. "Clip them onto your jeans as we go in," he instructed. He gazed at me. "You don't believe in curses, do you? You know — the ancient Egyptian kind."

I didn't know how to reply, so I shook my head.

"Good," Uncle Ben replied, grinning. "Because one of my workers claims we've violated an ancient decree by entering this new tunnel, and that we've activated some curse."

"We're not scared," Sari said, giving him a playful shove toward the entrance. "Get going, Dad."

And seconds later, we were stepping into the small, square opening cut into the stone. Stooping

159

low, I followed them through a narrow tunnel that seemed to slope gradually down.

Uncle Ben led the way, lighting the ground with a bright halogen flashlight. The pyramid floor was soft and sandy. The air was cool and damp.

"The walls are granite," Uncle Ben said, stopping to rub a hand along the low ceiling. "All of the tunnels were made of limestone."

The temperature dropped suddenly. The air felt even wetter. I suddenly realized why Uncle Ben had made us wear our sweatshirts.

"If you're scared, we can go back," Sari said.

"I'm fine," I replied quickly.

The tunnel ended abruptly. A pale yellow wall rose up in front of us. Ben's flashlight darted over a small, dark hole in the floor.

"Down we go," Ben said, groaning as he dropped to his knees. He turned back to me. "Afraid there are no stairs down to the new tunnel. My workers installed a rope ladder. Just take your time on it, take it slowly, one rung at a time, and you'll be fine."

"No problem," I said. But my voice cracked.

"Don't look down," Sari advised. "It might make you dizzy, and you'll fall."

"Thanks for the encouragement," I told her. I pushed my way past her. "I'll go down first," I said. I was already tired of her acting so superior. I decided to show her who was brave and who wasn't.

"No. Let me go first," Uncle Ben said, raising a hand to stop me. "Then I'll shine the light up at the ladder and help you down."

With another groan, he maneuvered himself into the hole. He was so big, he nearly didn't fit.

Slowly, he began to lower himself down the rope ladder.

Sari and I leaned over the hole and peered down, watching him descend. The rope ladder wasn't very steady. It swung back and forth under his weight as he slowly, carefully, made his way down.

"It's a long way down," I said softly.

Sari didn't reply. In the shadowy light, I could see her worried expression. She was chewing on her lower lip as her dad reached the tunnel floor.

She was nervous, too.

That cheered me up a lot.

"Okay, I'm down. You're next, Gabe," Uncle Ben called up to me.

I turned and swung my feet onto the rope ladder. I grinned at Sari. "See ya."

I lowered my hands to the sides of the rope ladder — and as I slid them down, I cried out.

"Ow!"

The rope wasn't smooth. It was coarse. It cut my hands.

The sharp stab of pain made me lift my hands.

And before I even realized what was happening, I started to fall.

4

Two hands reached down for mine. They shot through the air and grabbed my wrists.

"Hold on!" Sari cried.

She had slowed my fall just enough to allow me to grab back onto the sides of the rope ladder.

"Oh, wow!" I managed to utter. That was the best I could do. I gripped the rope for dear life, waiting for my heart to stop pounding. I closed my eyes and didn't move. I squeezed the ropes so hard, my hands ached.

"Saved your life," Sari called down to me, leaning into the opening, her face inches from mine.

I opened my eyes and stared up at her. "Thanks," I said gratefully.

"No problem," she replied and burst out laughing, laughing from relief, I guess.

Why couldn't I save *her* life? I asked myself angrily. Why can't *I* ever be the big hero?

"What happened, Gabe?" Uncle Ben called from the tunnel floor below. His booming voice echoed loudly through the chamber. The wide circle of light from his flashlight danced across the granite wall.

"The rope cut my hands," I explained. "I wasn't expecting — "

"Just take your time," he said patiently. "One rung at a time, remember?"

"Lower your hands. Don't slide them," Sari advised, her face poking through the hole above me.

"Okay, okay," I said, starting to breathe normally.

I took a deep breath and held it. Then, slowly, carefully, I made my way down the long rope ladder.

A short while later, all three of us were standing on the tunnel floor, holding our lighted flashlights, our eyes following the circles of light. "This way," Uncle Ben said quietly, and he headed off to the right, walking slowly, stooping because of the low ceiling.

Our sneakers crunched on the sandy floor. I saw another tunnel leading off to the right, then another tunnel on the left.

"We're breathing air that is four thousand years old," Ben said, keeping his light aimed on the floor ahead of him.

"Smells like it," I whispered to Sari. She laughed.

The air really did smell old. Kind of heavy and musty. Like someone's attic.

163

The tunnel widened a little as it curved to the right.

"We're going deeper into the earth," Ben said. "Does it feel like you're going downhill?"

Sari and I both muttered that it did.

"Dad and I explored one of the side tunnels yesterday," Sari told me. "We found a mummy case inside a tiny room. A beautiful one in perfect condition."

"Was there a mummy inside it?" I asked eagerly. I was dying to see a mummy. The museum back home had only one. I'd stared at it and studied it all my life.

"No. It was empty," Sari replied.

"Why didn't the mummy have any hobbies?" Uncle Ben asked, stopping suddenly.

"I don't know," I answered.

"He was too wrapped up in his work!" Uncle Ben exclaimed. He laughed at his own joke. Sari and I could only muster weak smiles.

"Don't encourage him," Sari told me, loud enough for her dad to hear. "He knows a million mummy jokes, and they're all just as bad."

"Wait up. Just a sec," I said. I bent down to tie my sneaker, which had come undone again.

The tunnel curved, then divided into two tunnels. Uncle Ben led us through the one on the left, which was so narrow we had to squeeze through it, making our way sideways, heads bent, until it widened into a large, high-ceilinged chamber.

I stood up straight and stretched. It felt so good not to be scrunched down. I stared around the large room.

Several people came into view at the far wall, working with digging tools. Bright spotlights had been hung above them on the wall, attached to a portable generator.

Uncle Ben brought us over to them and introduced us. There were four workers, two men and two women.

Another man stood off to the side, a clipboard in his hand. He was an Egyptian, dressed all in white except for a red bandanna around his neck. He had straight black hair, slicked down and tied in a ponytail behind his head. He stared at Sari and me, but didn't come over. He seemed to be studying us.

"Ahmed, you met my daughter yesterday. This is Gabe, my nephew," Uncle Ben called to him.

Ahmed nodded, but didn't smile or say anything.

"Ahmed is from the university," Uncle Ben explained to me in a low voice. "He requested permission to observe us, and I said okay. He's very quiet. But don't get him started on ancient curses. He's the one who keeps warning me that I'm in deadly danger."

Ahmed nodded, but didn't reply. He stared at me for a long while.

Weird guy, I thought.

I wondered if he'd tell me about the ancient curses. I loved stories about ancient curses.

Uncle Ben turned to his workers. "So? Any progress today?" he asked.

"We think we're getting real close," a young, red-haired man wearing faded jeans and a blue denim work shirt replied. And then he added, "Just a hunch."

Ben frowned. "Thanks, Quasimodo," he said.

The workers all laughed. I guess they liked Uncle Ben's jokes.

"Quasimodo was the Hunchback of Notre Dame," Sari explained to me in her superior tone.

"I know, I know," I replied irritably. "I get it."

"We could be heading in the wrong direction altogether," Uncle Ben told the workers, scratching the bald spot on the back of his head. "The tunnel might be over there." He pointed to the wall on the right.

"No, I think we're getting warm, Ben," a young woman, her face smudged with dust, said. "Come over here. I want to show you something."

She led him over to a large pile of stones and debris. He shined his light where she was pointing. Then he leaned closer to examine what she was showing him.

"That's very interesting, Christy," Uncle Ben said, rubbing his chin. They fell into a long discussion.

After a while, three other workers entered the

chamber, carrying shovels and picks. One of them was carrying some kind of electronic equipment in a flat metal case. It looked a little like a laptop computer.

I wanted to ask Uncle Ben what it was, but he was still in the corner, involved in his discussion with the worker named Christy.

Sari and I wandered back toward the tunnel entrance. "I think he's forgotten about us," Sari said sullenly.

I agreed, shining my flashlight up at the high, cracked ceiling.

"Once he gets down here with the workers, he forgets everything but his work," she said, sighing.

"I can't believe we're actually inside a pyramid!" I exclaimed.

Sari laughed. She kicked at the floor with one sneaker. "Look — ancient dirt," she said.

"Yeah." I kicked up some of the sandy dirt, too. "I wonder who walked here last. Maybe an Egyptian priestess. Maybe a pharaoh. They might have stood right here on this spot."

"Let's go exploring," Sari said suddenly.

"Huh?"

Her dark eyes gleamed, and she had a really devilish look on her face. "Let's go, Gabey — let's check out some tunnels or something."

"Don't call me Gabey," I said. "Come on, Sari, you know I hate that."

"Sorry," she apologized, giggling. "You coming?"

"We can't," I insisted, watching Uncle Ben. He was having some kind of argument with the worker carrying the thing that looked like a laptop. "Your dad said we had to stick together. He said — "

"He'll be busy here for hours," she interrupted, glancing back at him. "He won't even notice we're gone. Really."

"But, Sari — " I started.

"Besides," she continued, putting her hands on my shoulders and pushing me backwards toward the chamber door, "he doesn't want us hanging around. We'll only get in the way."

"Sari — "

"I went exploring yesterday," she said, pushing me with both hands. "We won't go far. You can't get lost. All the tunnels lead back to this big room. Really."

"I just don't think we should," I said, my eyes on Uncle Ben. He was down on his hands and knees now, digging against the wall with some kind of a pick.

"Let go of me," I told her. "Really. I — "

And then she said what I knew she'd say. What she *always* says when she wants to get her way.

"Are you chicken?"

"No," I insisted. "You know your dad said — "

"Chicken? Chicken? Chicken?" She began cluck-

168

ing like a chicken. Really obnoxious.

"Stop it, Sari." I tried to sound tough and menacing.

"Are you chicken, *Gabey*?" she repeated, grinning at me as if she'd just won some big victory. "Huh, *Gabey*?"

"Stop calling me that!" I insisted.

She just stared at me.

I made a disgusted face. "Okay, okay. Let's go exploring," I told her.

I mean, what else could I say?

"But not far," I added.

"Don't worry," she said, grinning. "We won't get lost. I'll just show you some of the tunnels I looked at yesterday. One of them has a strange animal picture carved on the wall. I think it's some kind of a cat. I'm not sure."

"Really?" I cried, instantly excited. "I've seen pictures of relief carvings, but I've never — "

"It may be a cat," Sari said. "Or maybe a person with an animal head. It's really weird."

"Where is it?" I asked.

"Follow me."

We both gave one last glance back to Uncle Ben, who was down on his hands and knees, picking away at the stone wall.

Then I followed Sari out of the chamber.

We squeezed through the narrow tunnel, then turned and followed a slightly wider tunnel to the right. I hesitated, a few steps behind her. "Are you sure we'll be able to get back?" I asked, keeping my voice low so she couldn't accuse me of sounding frightened.

"No problem," she replied. "Keep your light on the floor. There's a small chamber on the other ⁀nd of this tunnel that's kind of neat."

We followed the tunnel as it curved to the right. It branched into two low openings, and Sari took the one to the left.

The air grew a little warmer. It smelled stale, as if people had been smoking cigarettes there.

This tunnel was wider than the others. Sari was walking faster now, getting farther ahead of me. "Hey — wait up!" I cried.

I looked down to see that my sneaker had come untied again. Uttering a loud, annoyed groan, I bent to retie it.

"Hey, Sari, wait up!"

She didn't seem to hear me.

I could see her light in the distance, growing fainter in the tunnel.

Then it suddenly disappeared.

Had her flashlight burned out?

No. The tunnel probably curved, I decided. She's just out of my view.

"Hey, Sari!" I called. "Wait up! Wait *up*!"

I stared ahead into the dark tunnel.

"Sari?"

Why didn't she answer me?

5

"Sari!"

My voice echoed through the long, curving tunnel.

No reply.

I called again, and listened to my voice fading as the echo repeated her name again and again.

At first I was angry.

I knew what Sari was doing.

She was deliberately not answering, deliberately trying to frighten me.

She had to prove that she was the brave one, and I was the 'fraidy cat.

I suddenly remembered another time, a few years before. Sari and Uncle Ben had come to my house for a visit. I think Sari and I were seven or eight.

We went outside to play. It was a gray day, threatening rain. Sari had a jump rope and was showing off, as usual, showing me how good she was at it. Then, of course, when she let me try it, I tripped and fell, and she laughed like crazy.

I'd decided to get back at her by taking her to this deserted old house a couple blocks up the street. The kids in the neighborhood all believed the house was haunted. It was a neat place to sneak in and explore, although our parents were always warning us to stay away from it because it was falling apart and dangerous.

So I led Sari to this house and told her it was haunted. And we sneaked in through the broken basement window.

It got even darker out, and started to rain. It was perfect. I could tell Sari was really scared to be alone in the creepy old house. I, of course, wasn't scared at all because I'd been there before.

Well, we started exploring, with me leading the way. And somehow we got separated. And it started thundering and lightning outside. There was rain pouring in through the broken windows.

I decided maybe we should get home. So I called to Sari. No answer.

I called again. Still no answer.

Then I heard a loud crash.

Calling her name, I started running from room to room. I was scared to death. I was sure something terrible had happened.

I ran through every room in the house, getting more and more scared. I couldn't find her. I shouted and shouted, but she didn't answer me.

I was so scared, I started to cry. Then I totally

panicked, and I ran out of the house and into the pouring rain.

I ran through the thunder and lightning, crying all the way home. By the time I got home, I was soaked through and through.

I ran into the kitchen, sobbing and crying that I'd lost Sari in the haunted house.

And there she was. Sitting at the kitchen table. Comfortable and dry. Eating a big slice of chocolate cake. A smug smile on her face.

And now, peering into the darkness of the pyramid, I knew Sari was doing the same thing to me.

Trying to scare me.

Trying to make me look bad.

Or *was* she?

As I made my way through the low, narrow tunnel, keeping the light aimed straight ahead, I couldn't help it. My anger quickly turned to worry, and troubling questions whirred through my mind.

What if she *wasn't* playing a mean trick on me?

What if something bad *had* happened to her?

What if she had missed a step and fallen into a hole?

Or had gotten herself trapped in a hidden tunnel? Or . . . I didn't know what.

I wasn't thinking clearly.

My sneakers thudded loudly over the sandy floor as I started to half-walk, half-jog through the winding tunnel. "Sari?" I called, frantically now, not caring whether I sounded frightened or not.

Where was she?

She wasn't that far ahead of me. I should at least be able to see the light from her flashlight, I thought.

"Sari?"

There was no place for her to hide in this narrow space. Was I following the wrong tunnel?

No.

I had been in the same tunnel all along. The same tunnel I had watched her disappear in.

Don't say *disappear*, I scolded myself. Don't even *think* the word.

Suddenly the narrow tunnel ended. A small opening led into a small, square room. I flashed the light quickly from side to side.

"Sari?"

No sign of her.

The walls were bare. The air was warm and stale. I moved the flashlight rapidly across the floor, looking for Sari's footprints. The floor was harder, less sandy here. There were no footprints.

"Oh!"

I uttered a low cry when my light came to rest on the object against the far wall. My heart pounding, I eagerly took a few steps closer until I was just a few feet from it.

It was a mummy case.

A large, stone mummy case, at least eight feet long.

It was rectangular, with curved corners. The lid was carved. I stepped closer and aimed the light.

Yes.

A human face was carved on the lid. The face of a woman. It looked like a death mask, the kind we'd studied in school. It stared wide-eyed up at the ceiling.

"Wow!" I cried aloud. A real mummy case.

The carved face on the lid must have been brightly painted at one time. But the color had faded over the centuries. Now the face was gray, as pale as death.

Staring at the top of the case, smooth and perfect, I wondered if Uncle Ben had seen it. Or if I had made a discovery of my own.

Why is it all by itself in this small room? I wondered.

And what does it hold inside?

I was working up my courage to run my hand over the smooth stone of the lid when I heard the creaking sound.

And saw the lid start to raise up.

"Oh!" a hushed cry escaped my lips.

At first I thought I had imagined it. I didn't move a muscle. I kept the light trained on the lid.

The lid lifted a tiny bit more.

And I heard a hissing sound come from inside

the big coffin, like air escaping a new coffee can when you first open it.

Uttering another low cry, I took a step back.

The lid raised up another inch.

I took another step back.

And dropped the flashlight.

I picked it up with a trembling hand and shined it back onto the mummy case.

The lid was now open nearly a foot.

I sucked in a deep breath of air and held it.

I wanted to run, but my fear was freezing me in place.

I wanted to scream, but I knew I wouldn't be able to make a sound.

The lid creaked and opened another inch.

Another inch.

I lowered the flashlight to the opening, the light quivering with my hand.

From the dark depths of the ancient coffin, I saw two eyes staring out at me.

I uttered a silent gasp.

I froze.

I felt a cold chill zigzag down my back.

The lid slowly pushed open another inch.

The eyes stared out at me. Cold eyes. Evil eyes. Ancient eyes.

My mouth dropped open. And before I even realized it, I started to scream.

Scream at the top of my lungs.

As I screamed, unable to turn away, unable to run, unable to move, the lid slid open all the way.

Slowly, as if in a dream, a dark figure raised itself from the depths of the mummy case and climbed out.

"Sari!"

A broad smile widened across her face. Her eyes glowed gleefully.

"Sari — that wasn't funny!" I managed to shout in a high-pitched voice that bounced off the stone walls.

But now she was laughing too hard to hear me. Loud, scornful laughter.

I was so furious, I searched frantically for something to throw at her. But there wasn't anything, not even a pebble on the floor.

Staring at her, my chest still heaving from my fright, I really hated her then. She had made a total fool of me. There I had been, screaming like a baby.

I knew she'd never let me live it down.

Never.

"The look on your face!" she exclaimed when she finally stopped laughing. "I wish I had a camera."

I was too angry to reply. I just growled at her.

I pulled the little mummy hand from my back pocket and began rolling it around in my hand. I always fiddled with that hand when I was upset. It usually helped to calm me.

But now I felt as if I'd *never* calm down.

"I *told* you I'd found an empty mummy case yesterday," she said, brushing the hair back off her face. "Didn't you remember?"

I growled again.

I felt like a total dork.

First I'd fallen for her dad's stupid mummy costume. And now this.

Silently to myself I vowed to pay her back. If it was the last thing I ever did.

She was still chuckling about her big-deal joke.

"The look on your face," she said again, shaking her head. Rubbing it in.

"You wouldn't like it if I scared you," I muttered angrily.

"You *couldn't* scare me," she replied. "I don't scare so easy."

"Hah!"

That was the best comeback I could think of. Not very clever, I know. But I was too angry to be clever.

I was imagining myself picking Sari up and tossing her back into the mummy case, pulling down the lid, and locking it — when I heard footsteps approaching in the tunnel.

Glancing over at Sari, I saw her expression change. She heard them, too.

A few seconds later, Uncle Ben burst into the small room. I could see immediately, even in the dim light, that he was really angry.

"I thought I could trust you two," he said, talking through gritted teeth.

"Dad — " Sari started.

But he cut her off sharply. "I trusted you not to wander off without telling me. Do you know how easy it is to get lost in this place? Lost forever?"

"Dad," Sari started again. "I was just showing Gabe this room I discovered yesterday. We were going to come right back. Really."

"There are *hundreds* of tunnels," Uncle Ben

said heatedly, ignoring Sari's explanation. "Maybe thousands. Many of them have never been explored. No one has ever been in this section of the pyramid before. We have no idea what dangers there are. You two can't just wander off by yourselves. Do you know how frantic I was when I turned around and you were gone?"

"Sorry," Sari and I both said in unison.

"Let's go," Uncle Ben said, gesturing to the door with his flashlight. "Your pyramid visit is over for today."

We followed him into the tunnel. I felt really bad. Not only had I fallen for Sari's stupid joke, but I'd made my favorite uncle really angry.

Sari always gets me into trouble, I thought bitterly. Since we were little kids.

Now she was walking ahead of me, arm in arm with her dad, telling him something, her face close to his ear. Suddenly they both burst out laughing and turned back to look at me.

I could feel my face getting hot.

I knew what she'd told him.

She'd told him about hiding in the mummy case and making me scream like a scared baby. And now they were both chuckling about what a jerk I was.

"Merry Christmas to you, too!" I called bitterly.

And that made them laugh even harder.

* * *

180

We spent the night back in the hotel in Cairo. I beat Sari in two straight games of Scrabble, but it didn't make me feel any better.

She kept complaining that she had only vowels, and so the games weren't fair. Finally, I put my Scrabble set back in my room, and we sat and stared at the TV.

The next morning, we had breakfast in the room. I ordered pancakes, but they didn't taste like any pancakes I'd ever eaten. They were tough and grainy, as if they were made of cowhide or something.

"What are we doing today?" Sari asked Uncle Ben, who was still yawning and stretching after two cups of black coffee.

"I have an appointment at the Cairo Museum," he told us, glancing at his wristwatch. "It's just a couple of blocks away. I thought you two might like to wander around the museum while I have my meeting."

"Ooh, thrills and chills," Sari said sarcastically. She slurped up another spoonful of Frosted Flakes.

The little Frosted Flakes box had Arabic writing all over it, and Tony the Tiger was saying something in Arabic. I wanted to save it and take it home to show my friends. But I knew Sari would make fun of me if I asked her for it, so I didn't.

"The museum has an interesting mummy collection, Gabe," Uncle Ben said to me. He tried to pour himself a third cup of coffee, but the pot was empty. "You'll like it."

"Unless they climb out of their cases," Sari said. Lame. Really lame.

I stuck my tongue out at her. She tossed a wet Frosted Flake across the table at me.

"When are my mom and dad getting back?" I asked Uncle Ben. I suddenly realized I missed them.

He started to answer, but the phone rang. He walked into the bedroom and picked it up. It was an old-fashioned black telephone with a dial instead of buttons. As he talked, his face filled with concern.

"Change of plans," he said a few seconds later, hanging up the receiver and coming back into the living room.

"What's the matter, Daddy?" Sari asked, shoving her cereal bowl away.

"It's very strange," he replied, scratching the back of his head. "Two of my workers came down sick last night. Some kind of mysterious illness." His expression became thoughtful, worried. "They took them to a hospital here in Cairo."

He started to gather up his wallet and some other belongings. "I think I'd better get over there right away," he said.

"But what about Gabe and me?" Sari asked, glancing at me.

182

"I'll only be gone an hour or so," her dad replied. "Stay here in the room, okay?"

"In the *room*?" Sari cried, making it sound like a punishment.

"Well, okay. You can go down to the lobby, if you want. But don't leave the hotel."

A few minutes later, he pulled on his tan safari jacket, checked one last time to make sure he had his wallet and keys, and hurried out the door.

Sari and I stared at each other glumly. "What do you want to do?" I asked, poking the cold, uneaten pancakes on my plate with a fork.

Sari shrugged. "Is it hot in here?"

I nodded. "Yeah. It's about a hundred and twenty."

"We have to get out of here," she said, standing up and stretching.

"You mean go down to the lobby?" I asked, still poking the pancakes, pulling them into pieces with the fork.

"No. I mean get *out* of here," she replied. She walked over to the mirror in the entranceway and began brushing her straight, black hair.

"But Uncle Ben said — " I started.

"We won't go far," she said, and then quickly added, "if you're afraid."

I made a face at her. I don't think she saw me. She was busy admiring herself in the mirror.

"Okay," I told her. "We could go to the museum. Your dad said it was just a block away."

I was determined not to be the wimp anymore. If she wanted to disobey her dad and go out, fine with me. From now on, I decided, *I'll* be the macho guy. No repeats of yesterday — ever again.

"The museum?" She made a face. "Well . . . okay," she said, turning to look at me. "We're twelve, after all. It's not like we're babies. We can go out if we want."

"Yes, we can," I said. "I'll write Uncle Ben a note and tell him where we're going, in case he gets back before we do." I went over to the desk and picked up a pen and a small pad of paper.

"If you're afraid, *Gabey*, we can just walk around the block," she said in a teasing voice, staring at me, waiting to see how I'd react.

"No way," I said. "We're going to the museum. Unless *you're* afraid."

"No way," she said, imitating me.

"And don't call me Gabey," I added.

"Gabey, Gabey, Gabey," she muttered, just to be annoying.

I wrote the note to Uncle Ben. Then we took the elevator down to the lobby. We asked a young woman behind the desk where the Cairo Museum was. She said to turn right outside the hotel and walk two blocks.

Sari hesitated as we stepped out into the bright sunshine. "You sure you're up for this?"

"What could go wrong?" I replied.

7

"Let's go. This way," I said, shielding my eyes from the bright sunlight with my hand.

"It's so hot," Sari complained.

The street was crowded and noisy. I couldn't hear anything over the honking of car horns.

Drivers here lean on their horns the minute they start up their cars, and they don't stop honking till they arrive at their destinations.

Sari and I stayed close together, making our way through the crush of people on the sidewalk. All kinds of people passed by.

There were men in American-style business suits walking alongside men who appeared to be wearing loose-fitting white pajamas.

We saw women who would look right at home on any street in America, wearing colorful leggings and stylish skirts and slacks. Women in jeans. Followed by women dressed in long, flowing black dresses, their faces covered by heavy, black veils.

"This sure doesn't look like back home!" I exclaimed, shouting over the blare of car horns.

I was so fascinated by all the interesting-looking people crowding the narrow sidewalk that I forgot to look at the buildings. Before I knew it, we were standing in front of the museum, a tall, stone structure looming above the street behind steeply sloping steps.

We climbed the steps and entered the revolving door of the museum.

"Wow, it's so quiet in here!" I exclaimed, whispering. It was nice to get away from the honking horns, the crowded sidewalks, and shouting people.

"Why do you think they honk their horns so much?" Sari asked, holding her ears.

"Just a custom, I guess," I replied.

We stopped and looked around.

We were standing in the center of an enormous open lobby. Tall marble stairways rose up on the far left and far right. Twin white columns framed a wide doorway that led straight back. An enormous mural across the wall to the right showed an aerial view of the pyramids and the Nile.

We stood in the middle of the floor, admiring the mural for a while. Then we made our way to the back wall and asked a woman at the information desk for the mummy room. She flashed us a nice smile and told us in perfect English to take the stairs to the right.

Our sneakers thudded loudly over the shiny

marble floor. The stairway seemed to go up forever. "This is like mountain climbing," I complained, halfway up.

"Race you to the top," Sari said, grinning, and took off before I had a chance to reply.

Of course she beat me by about ten steps.

I waited for her to call me "slowpoke" or "snail face" or something. But she had already turned to see what lay ahead of us.

A dark, high-ceilinged room seemed to stretch on forever. A glass case stood centered in the entryway. Inside was a detailed construction of wood and clay.

I went up close to take a good look. The construction showed thousands of workers dragging enormous blocks of limestone across the sand toward a partially built pyramid.

In the room behind the display I could see huge stone statues, large mummy cases, displays of glass and pottery, and case after case of artifacts and relics.

"I think this is the place!" I exclaimed happily, rushing over to the first display case.

"Ooh, what's that? Some kind of giant dog?" Sari asked, pointing to an enormous statue against the wall.

The creature appeared to have a fierce dog's head and a lion's body. Its eyes stared straight ahead, and it seemed ready to pounce on anyone who came near it.

"They put creatures like that in front of tombs," I told Sari. "You know. To protect the place. Scare away grave robbers."

"Like guard dogs," Sari said, stepping up close to the ancient sculpture.

"Hey — there's a mummy in this case!" I exclaimed, leaning over an ancient stone coffin. "Look!"

Still staring back at the enormous sculpture, Sari walked up beside me. "Yep. It's a mummy, okay," she said, unimpressed. I guess she's seen a lot more of them than me.

"It's so small," I said, staring at the yellowed linen wrapped so tightly around the skinny head and body.

"Our ancestors were shrimps," Sari replied. "Think it was a man or a woman?"

I glanced at the plaque on the side of the coffin. "It says it's a man."

"Guess they didn't work out in those days," she said and laughed at her own remark.

"They did a great wrapping job," I said, examining the carefully wrapped fingers on the hands, which were crossed over the mummy's chest. "I was a mummy the Halloween before last, and my costume completely unraveled after ten minutes!"

Sari tsk-tsked.

"Do you know how they made mummies?" I

asked, moving around to view it from the other side. "Do you know the first thing they did? They removed the brain."

"Yuck. Stop," she said, sticking out her tongue and making a disgusted face.

"Don't you *know* about this?" I asked, delighted that I had some truly gruesome information that she didn't.

"Please — enough," she said, holding up one hand as if to fend me off.

"No, this is interesting," I insisted. "The brain had to come out first. They had this special tool. It was like a long, skinny hook. They'd push it up the corpse's nose until it reached the brain and then wiggled it back and forth, back and forth, until the brain became mush."

"*Stop!*" Sari pleaded, covering her ears.

"Then they took a long spoon," I continued gleefully, "and scooped the brain out a little at a time."

I made a scooping motion with my hand. "Scoop scoop. They scooped the brain out through the nose. Or sometimes they popped off an eyeball and scooped the brain out through the eyeball socket."

"Gabe — I *mean* it!" Sari cried. She really looked like she was about to hurl. She was green!

I loved it.

I never knew that Sari had a squeamish bone in her body. But I was really making her sick.

Outstanding! I thought.

I would definitely have to remember this technique.

"It's all true," I told her, unable to hold back a wide grin.

"Just shut up," she muttered.

"Of course sometimes they didn't pull the brain out the nose. Sometimes they just sliced off the head. Then they drained the brains out through the neck and put the head back on the body. They just bandaged it back on, I guess."

"Gabe — "

I'd been staring at her the whole time, checking out her reaction. She was looking sicker and sicker. She was breathing real heavy. Her chest was sort of heaving. I really thought she was going to lose her breakfast.

If she did, I'd never let her forget it.

"That's really gross," she said. Her voice sounded funny, like it was coming from underwater or something.

"But it's true," I said. "Didn't your dad ever tell you about how they made mummies?"

She shook her head. "He knows I don't like — "

"And you know what they did with the guts?" I asked, enjoying the startled look on her face. "They put them in jars and — "

I suddenly realized that Sari's startled look wasn't for me.

She was actually staring over my shoulder.

"Huh?" I turned around and saw why she suddenly looked so surprised.

A man had entered the room and was standing just in front of the first display case. It took me a few seconds to recognize him.

It was Ahmed, the strange, silent Egyptian with the black ponytail who had greeted us in such an unfriendly manner down inside the pyramid. He was dressed the same, in loose-fitting white trousers and shirt with a scarlet bandanna around his neck. And his expression was just as unfriendly. Angry, even.

Sari and I both backed away from the mummy case, and Ahmed, his eyes darting from one of us to the other, took a step toward us.

"Gabe, he's coming after us!" Sari whispered.

She grabbed my arm. Her hand was cold as ice.

"Let's get out of here!" she cried.

I hesitated. Shouldn't we stop and say hello to him first?

But something about the stern, determined look on Ahmed's face told me that Sari was right.

We turned and began walking really fast away from him into the vast room, Sari a few steps ahead of me.

I turned and saw that Ahmed was jogging after us.

He shouted something to us, his voice angry, threatening. I couldn't make out the words.

"Run!" Sari cried.

And now we were both running at full speed, our sneakers drumming loudly over the polished marble floor.

We scooted around an enormous glass display case containing three upright mummy cases. Then we ran straight down the wide aisle between sculptures and shelves of ancient pottery and pyramid relics.

Behind us, I could hear Ahmed shouting furiously, "Come back! Come back!"

He sounded really angry.

His shoes clacked against the floor as he ran, the sound echoing in the vast, empty museum chamber.

"He's gaining on us!" I called to Sari, who was still a few steps ahead.

"There's got to be a way *out* of here!" she answered breathlessly.

But I immediately saw that there wasn't. We were nearly to the back wall. We passed a gigantic sphinx, then stopped.

There was nowhere to go.

No doorway. No exit.

A solid granite wall.

We both turned and saw Ahmed's eyes grow wide with triumph.

He had us cornered.

8

Ahmed stopped a few feet in front of us. He was panting like a dog, gasping for air, and holding his side. He glared at us angrily.

Sari glanced at me. She looked pale, really frightened. We both had our backs pressed against the wall.

I swallowed hard. My throat felt tight and dry.

What was he going to do to us?

"Why did you run?" Ahmed finally managed to say, still holding his side as if he had a cramp. "Why?"

We didn't reply. We both stared back at him, waiting to see what he was about to do.

"I came with a message from your father," he told Sari, breathing hard. He raised the red bandanna from his neck and wiped his perspiring forehead with it. "Why did you run?"

"A message?" Sari stammered.

"Yes," Ahmed said. "You know me. We met again yesterday. I don't understand why you ran."

"I'm sorry," Sari said quickly, glancing guiltily at me.

"We weren't thinking clearly," I said. "Sari frightened me, and I followed her."

"Gabe was telling me all this frightening stuff," she said, jabbing me hard in the side with her elbow. "It was *his* fault. He scared me with all this mummy stuff. So when I saw you, I wasn't thinking clearly, and . . ."

Both of us were babbling. We both felt so relieved that he wasn't chasing us — and so embarrassed that we had run away from him.

"Your father sent me to get you," Ahmed said, his dark eyes trained on me. "I didn't think I'd have to chase you through the whole museum."

"Sorry," Sari and I said in unison.

I felt like a complete jerk. I'm sure Sari did, too.

"Daddy came back to the hotel and saw Gabe's note?" Sari asked, straightening her hair with her hand as she moved away from the wall.

"Yes." Ahmed nodded.

"He got back from the hospital awfully fast," Sari said, glancing at her wristwatch.

"Yes," Ahmed replied again. "Come. I will take you back to the hotel. He is waiting for you there."

We followed him in silence, Sari and I walking side by side a few steps behind him.

As we made our way down the long stairway, we glanced sheepishly at each other. We were both feeling really foolish for running away like that.

A short while later, we were back on the crowded, noisy sidewalk, an unending stream of cars honking past, all moving in starts and stops, drivers hanging out of car windows, shouting and shaking their fists.

Ahmed checked to make sure we were with him, then turned right and began leading the way through the crowd. The sun was high over the buildings now. The air was hot and humid.

"Hey, wait — " I called.

Ahmed turned back, but kept walking.

"We're going the wrong way," I called to him, shouting over the cries of a street peddler behind a cart of vegetables. "The hotel is back that way." I pointed.

Ahmed shook his head. "My car is just up there."

"We're driving back to the hotel?" Sari asked, her voice revealing her surprise.

"It's only two blocks," I said to Ahmed. "Sari and I could walk back by ourselves if you want. You really don't have to take us."

"It is no trouble," Ahmed replied, and he placed his hands firmly, one on my shoulder, one on Sari's, and continued to guide us to his car.

We crossed the street and continued walking. The sidewalk grew even more crowded. A man swinging a leather briefcase accidentally clipped my shoulder with it. I cried out in pain.

Sari laughed.

"You have a great sense of humor," I muttered sarcastically.

"I know," she replied.

"If we'd walked, we would have been at the hotel already," I said.

Ahmed must have overheard, because he said, "The car's in the next block."

We made our way quickly through the crowds. A short while later, Ahmed stopped at a small, four-door stationwagon. It was covered with dust, and the fender on the driver's side was crunched.

He pulled open the back door, and Sari and I piled in. "Ow," I complained. The leather seats were burning hot.

"The wheel is hot, too," Ahmed said, climbing in and fastening his seat belt. He touched the steering wheel a few times with both hands, trying to get used to the heat. "They should invent a car that stays cool inside when it is parked."

The engine started on the second try, and he pulled away from the curb and into the line of traffic.

Immediately, he began honking the horn at the car in front of us. We moved slowly, stopping every few seconds, through the narrow street.

"I wonder why Daddy didn't come to get us," Sari said to me, her eyes on the crowds passing by the dusty car window.

"He said he would wait for you at the hotel," Ahmed replied from the front seat.

He made a sudden sharp turn onto a wider avenue and began to pick up speed.

It took me a long while to realize that we were heading in the wrong direction — *away* from our hotel. "Uh . . . Ahmed . . . I think the hotel is back that way," I said, pointing toward the back window.

"I believe you are mistaken," he replied softly, staring straight ahead through the windshield. "We will be there shortly."

"No. Really," I insisted.

One thing about me is I have a really good sense of direction. Mom and Dad always say they don't need a map when I'm around. I almost always know when I'm heading the wrong way.

Sari turned to glance at me, an expression of concern beginning to tighten her features.

"Settle back and enjoy the ride," Ahmed said, staring at me through the rearview mirror. "Have you fastened your seat belts? Better do it right now."

He had a smile on his face, but his voice was cold. His words sounded like a threat.

"Ahmed, we've gone too far," I insisted, starting to feel really afraid.

Outside the window, the buildings were lower, more rundown. We seemed to be heading away from the downtown area.

"Just settle back," he replied with growing impatience. "I know where I'm going."

Sari and I exchanged glances. She looked as worried as I did. We both realized that Ahmed was lying to us. He wasn't taking us to the hotel. He was taking us out of town.

We were being kidnapped.

9

Seeing Ahmed's eyes on me in the rearview mirror, I fiddled with the seat belt, pretending to fasten it. As I did this, I leaned close to Sari and whispered in her ear, "Next time he stops."

At first she didn't get my meaning. But then I saw that she understood.

We both sat tensely, eyes on the door handles, waiting in silence.

"Your father is a very smart man," Ahmed said, staring at Sari in the mirror.

"I know," Sari replied in a tiny voice.

The traffic slowed, then stopped.

"Now!" I screamed.

We both grabbed for the door handles.

I pushed my door open and flung myself out of the car.

Horns were honking in front of me and behind me. I could hear Ahmed's surprised shout.

Leaving the car door open, I turned to see that Sari had made it to the street, too. She turned to me as she slammed her door shut, her eyes wide with fear.

Without a word, we started to run.

The car horns seemed to grow louder as we headed into a narrow side street. We were running side by side, following the narrow brick street as it curved between two rows of tall, white stucco buildings.

I feel like a rat in a maze, I thought.

The street grew even narrower. Then it emptied into a wide circle filled with a small market of fruit and vegetable stands.

"Is he following us?" Sari cried, a few steps behind me now.

I turned back and searched for him, my eyes darting through the small crowd attending the market.

I saw several people in flowing white robes. Two women entered the market, dressed in black, carrying a basket loaded high with bananas. A boy on a bicycle swerved to keep from running straight into them.

"I don't see him," I called back to Sari.

But we kept running just to make sure.

I'd never been so scared in my life.

Please, *please*, I begged silently, don't let him be following us. Don't let him catch us!

Turning a corner, we found ourselves on a wide, busy avenue. A truck bounced past, pulling a trailer filled with horses. The sidewalk was crowded with shoppers and businesspeople.

Sari and I pushed our way through them, trying to lose ourselves in the crowd.

Finally, we came to a stop near the entrance of what appeared to be a large department store. Breathing hard, I rested my hands on my knees, leaned forward, and tried to catch my breath.

"We've lost him," Sari said, staring back in the direction from which we'd come.

"Yeah. We're okay," I said happily. I smiled at her, but she didn't return the smile.

Her face was filled with fear. Her eyes continued to stare into the crowd. One hand tugged nervously at a strand of her hair.

"We're okay," I repeated. "We got away."

"There's only one problem," she said quietly, her eyes still on the crowd bustling toward us on the sidewalk.

"Huh? Problem?"

"Now we're lost," she replied, finally turning to face me. "We're lost, Gabe. We don't know where we are."

I suddenly had a heavy feeling in the pit of my stomach. I started to utter a frightened cry.

But I forced myself to hold it in.

I forced myself to pretend I wasn't afraid.

Sari had always been the brave one, the winner, the champ. And I was always the wimp. But now

I could see that she was really scared. This was my chance to be the cool one, my chance to show her who was really the champ.

"No problem," I told her, gazing up at the tall glass and concrete buildings. "We'll just ask somebody to direct us to the hotel."

"But no one speaks English!" she cried, sounding as if she were about to cry.

"Uh . . . no problem," I said, a little less cheerily. "I'm sure someone . . ."

"We're lost," she repeated miserably, shaking her head. "Totally lost."

And then I saw the answer to our problem parked at the curb. It was a taxi, an empty taxi.

"Come on," I said, tugging her arm. I pulled her to the taxi. The driver, a thin, young man with a wide black mustache and stringy black hair falling out of a small gray cap, turned around in surprise as Sari and I climbed into the back seat.

"The Cairo Center Hotel," I said, glancing reassuringly at Sari.

The driver stared back at me blankly, as if he didn't understand.

"Please take us to the Cairo Center Hotel," I repeated slowly and clearly.

And then he tossed back his head, opened his mouth, and started to laugh.

10

The driver laughed till tears formed in the corners of his eyes.

Sari grabbed my arm. "He's working for Ahmed," she whispered, squeezing my wrist. "We've walked right into a trap!"

"Huh?" I felt a stab of fear in my chest.

I didn't think she was right.

She *couldn't* be right!

But I didn't know what else to think.

I grabbed the door handle and started to leap out of the taxi. But the driver raised a hand, signaling for me to stop.

"Gabe — *go!*" Sari pushed me hard from behind.

"Cairo Center Hotel?" the driver asked suddenly, wiping the tears from his eyes with a finger. Then he pointed through the windshield. "Cairo Center Hotel?"

Sari and I both followed his finger.

There was the hotel. Right across the street.

He started to laugh again, shaking his head.

"Thanks," I shouted, and climbed out.

Sari scrambled out behind me, a wide, relieved smile on her face. "I don't think it's *that* funny," I told her. "The cab driver has a strange sense of humor."

I turned back. The driver was still staring at us, a broad smile on his face.

"Come on," she urged, tugging at my arm. "We have to tell Daddy about Ahmed."

But to our surprise, our hotel room was empty. My note was still on the table where I had left it. Nothing had been moved or touched.

"He hasn't been back here," Sari said, picking up my note and crumpling it into a ball in her hand. "Ahmed lied — about everything."

I flopped down on the couch with a loud sigh. "I wonder what's going on," I said unhappily. "I just don't get it."

Sari and I both screamed as the door to the room flew open.

"Daddy!" Sari cried, running to hug him.

I was sure glad it was Uncle Ben, and not Ahmed.

"Daddy, the strangest thing — " Sari started.

Uncle Ben had his arm around her shoulder. As he led her across the room toward the couch, I could see that he had a really dazed expression on his face.

"Yes, it's strange," he muttered, shaking his head. "Both of my workers . . ."

"Huh? Are they okay?" Sari asked.

"No. Not really," Uncle Ben replied, dropping onto the arm of the armchair, staring hard but not really focusing on me. "They're both . . . in a state of shock. I guess that's how to describe it."

"They were in an accident? In the pyramid?" I asked.

Uncle Ben scratched the bald spot at the back of his head. "I don't really know. They can't talk. They're both . . . speechless. I think something — or someone — frightened them. Scared them speechless. The doctors are completely confused. They said that — "

"Daddy, Ahmed tried to kidnap us!" Sari interrupted, squeezing his hand.

"What? Ahmed?" He narrowed his eyes, his forehead wrinkling up in confusion. "What do you mean?"

"Ahmed. The guy at the pyramid. The one who wears the white suits with the red bandanna and always carries the clipboard," Sari explained.

"He told us you sent him to get us," I said. "He came to the museum — "

"Museum?" Uncle Ben climbed to his feet. "What were you doing at the museum? I thought I told you — "

"We had to get out of here," Sari said, putting a hand on her dad's shoulder, trying to calm him. "Gabe wanted to see mummies, so we went to the museum. But Ahmed came and took us to his car.

205

He said he was taking us to you at the hotel."

"But he was driving the wrong way," I continued the story. "So we jumped out and ran away."

"Ahmed?" Uncle Ben kept repeating the name, as if he just couldn't believe it. "He came to me with excellent credentials and references," he said. "He's a cryptographer. He studies ancient Egyptian. He's mainly interested in the wall writings and symbols we uncover."

"So why did he come for us?" I asked.

"Where was he going to take us?" Sari asked.

"I don't know," Uncle Ben said. "But I certainly intend to find out." He hugged Sari. "What a mystery," he continued. "You're both okay?"

"Yeah. We're okay," I replied.

"I've got to get to the pyramid," he said, letting go of Sari and walking to the window. "I gave my workers the day off. But I've got to get to the bottom of this."

Clouds rolled over the sun. The room suddenly grew darker.

"I'll order up some room service for you," Uncle Ben said, a thoughtful expression on his face. "Will you two be okay here till I get back tonight?"

"No!" Sari cried. "You can't leave us here!"

"Why can't we come with you?" I asked.

"Yes! We're coming with you!" Sari exclaimed, before Uncle Ben had a chance to reply.

He shook his head. "Too dangerous," he said, his eyes narrowing as he glanced first at me, then

206

at Sari. "Until I can find out what happened to my two workers in there — "

"But, Daddy, what if Ahmed comes back?" Sari cried, sounding really frightened. "What if he comes here?"

Uncle Ben scowled. "Ahmed," he muttered. "Ahmed."

"You can't leave us here!" Sari repeated.

Uncle Ben stared out the window at the darkening sky. "I guess you're right," he said finally. "I guess I have to take you with me."

"Yes!" Sari and I both cried, relieved.

"But you have to promise to stick close," Uncle Ben said sternly, pointing a finger at Sari. "I mean it. No wandering off. No more practical jokes."

I realized I was seeing a whole new side of my uncle. Even though he was a well-known scientist, he had always been the jolly practical joker of the family.

But now he was worried.

Seriously worried.

No more jokes until the frightening mystery was cleared up.

We had sandwiches downstairs in the hotel restaurant, then drove through the desert to the pyramid.

Heavy clouds rolled across the sun as we drove, casting shadows over the sand, coloring the desert darkly in shimmering shades of blue and gray.

Before long, the enormous pyramid loomed on

the horizon, appearing to grow larger as we approached on the nearly empty highway.

I remembered the first time I had seen it, just a few days before. Such an amazing sight.

But now, watching it through the car windshield, I felt only dread.

Uncle Ben parked the car near the low entrance he had discovered behind the pyramid. As we stepped out, the wind whipped at the ground, tossing the sand up, whirling it around our legs.

Uncle Ben raised a hand to stop us at the tunnel entrance.

"Here," he said. He reached into his supply pack and pulled out equipment for Sari and me. "Clip this on."

He handed each of us a beeper. "Just push the button, and it will beep me," he said, helping me clip mine to the belt on my jeans. "It's like a homing device. If you push the button, it sends electronic signals to the unit I'm wearing. Then I can track you down by following the sound levels. Of course, I don't expect you to use it because I expect you to stay close to me."

He handed us flashlights. "Watch your step," he instructed. "Keep the light down at your feet, a few yards ahead of you on the floor."

"We *know*, Daddy," Sari said. "We've done this before, remember?"

"Just follow instructions," he said sharply, and turned into the darkness of the pyramid opening.

I stopped at the entrance and pulled out my little mummy hand, just to make sure I had it.

"What are you doing with that?" Sari asked, making a face.

"My good luck charm," I said, slipping it back into my pocket.

She groaned and gave me a playful shove into the pyramid entrance.

A few minutes later, we were once again making our way carefully down the long rope ladder and into the first narrow tunnel.

Uncle Ben led the way, the wide circle of light from his flashlight sweeping back and forth across the tunnel ahead of him. Sari was a few steps behind him, and I walked a few steps behind her.

The tunnel seemed narrower and lower this time. I guess it was just my mood.

Gripping the flashlight tightly, keeping the light aimed down, I dipped my head to keep from hitting the low, curved ceiling.

The tunnel bent to the left, then sloped downhill where it split into two paths. We followed the one to the right. The only sound was that of our shoes scraping against the sandy, dry floor.

Uncle Ben coughed.

Sari said something. I couldn't hear what it was.

I had stopped to shine my light on a bunch of spiders on the ceiling, and the two of them had walked several yards ahead of me.

Following my light as it moved over the floor,

I saw that my sneaker had come untied once again.

"Oh, man — not again!"

I stooped to tie it, setting the flashlight on the ground beside me. "Hey — wait up!" I called.

But they had started to argue about something, and I don't think they heard me. I could hear their voices echoing loudly down the long, twisting tunnel, but I couldn't make out their words.

I hurriedly double-knotted the shoe lace, grabbed up the flashlight, and climbed to my feet. "Hey, wait up!" I shouted anxiously.

Where had they gone?

I realized that I couldn't hear their voices anymore.

This *can't* be happening to me again! I thought.

"Hey!" I shouted, cupping my hands over my mouth. My voice echoed down the tunnel.

But no voices called back.

"Wait up!"

Typical, I thought.

They were so involved in their argument, they forgot all about me.

I realized that I was more angry than frightened. Uncle Ben had made such a big deal about us sticking close together. And then he walked off and left me alone in the tunnel.

"Hey, where *are* you?" I shouted.

No reply.

11

Beaming the light ahead of me on the floor, I ducked my head and began jogging, following the tunnel as it curved sharply to the right.

The floor began to slope upwards. The air became hot and musty smelling. I found myself gasping for breath.

"Uncle Ben!" I called. "Sari!"

They must be around the next curve in the tunnel, I told myself. It hadn't taken me that long to tie my shoelace. They couldn't have gotten that far ahead.

Hearing a sound, I stopped.

And listened.

Silence now.

Was I starting to hear things?

I had a sudden flash: Was this another mean practical joke? Were Sari and Uncle Ben hiding, waiting to see what I'd do?

Was this another lame trick of theirs to frighten me?

It could be. Uncle Ben, I knew, could never resist a practical joke. He had laughed like a hyena when Sari told him how she'd hid in the mummy case and scared about ten years off my life.

Were they both hiding in mummy cases now, just waiting for me to stumble by?

My heart thumped in my chest. Despite the heat of the ancient tunnel, I felt cold all over.

No, I decided. This isn't a practical joke.

Uncle Ben was too serious today, too worried about his stricken workers. Too worried about what we'd told him about Ahmed. He wasn't in any mood for practical jokes.

I began making my way through the tunnel again. As I jogged, my hand brushed against the beeper at my waist.

Should I push it?

No, I decided.

That would only give Sari a good laugh. She'd be eager to tell everyone how I'd started beeping for help after being in the pyramid for two minutes!

I turned the corner. The tunnel walls seemed to close in on me as the tunnel narrowed.

"Sari? Uncle Ben?"

No echo. Maybe the tunnel was too narrow for an echo.

The floor grew harder, less sandy. In the dim yellow light, I could see that the granite walls were lined with jagged cracks. They looked like

212

dark lightning bolts coming down from the ceiling.

"Hey — where *are* you guys?" I shouted.

I stopped when the tunnel branched in two directions.

I suddenly realized how scared I was.

Where had they disappeared to? They *had* to have realized by now that I wasn't with them.

I stared at the two openings, shining my light first into one tunnel, then the other.

Which one had they entered?

Which one?

My heart pounding, I ran into the tunnel on the left and shouted their names.

No reply.

I backed out quickly, my light darting wildly over the floor, and stepped into the tunnel to the right.

This tunnel was wider and higher. It curved gently to the right.

A maze of tunnels. That's how Uncle Ben had described the pyramid. Maybe thousands of tunnels, he had told me.

Thousands.

Keep moving, I urged myself.

Keep moving, Gabe.

They're right up ahead. They've *got* to be!

I took a few steps and then called out to them.

I heard something.

Voices?

I stopped. It was so quiet now. So quiet, I could

213

hear my heart pounding in my chest.

The sound again.

I listened hard, holding my breath.

It was a chattering sound. A soft chittering. Not a human voice. An insect, maybe. Or a rat.

"Uncle Ben? Sari?"

Silence.

I took a few more steps into the tunnel. Then a few more.

I decided I'd better forget my pride and beep them.

So what if Sari teased me about it?

I was too frightened to care.

If I beeped them, they'd be right there to get me in a few seconds.

But as I reached to my waist for the beeper, I was startled by a loud noise.

The insect chittering became a soft *cracking* sound.

I stopped to listen, the fear rising up to my throat.

The soft cracking grew louder.

It sounded like someone breaking saltines in two.

Only louder. Louder.

Louder.

Right under my feet.

I turned my eyes to the floor.

I shined the light at my shoes.

214

It took me so long to realize what was happening.

The ancient tunnel floor was cracking apart beneath me.

The cracking grew louder, seemed to come from all directions, to surround me.

By the time I realized what was happening, it was too late.

I felt as if I were being pulled down, sucked down by a powerful force.

The floor crumbled away beneath me, and I was falling.

Falling down, down, down an endless black hole.

I opened my mouth to scream, but no sound came out.

My hands flew up and grabbed — nothing!

I closed my eyes and fell.

Down, down into the swirling blackness.

12

I heard the flashlight clang against the floor.

Then I hit. Hard.

I landed on my side. Pain shot through my body, and I saw red. A flash of bright red that grew brighter and brighter until I had to close my eyes. I think the force of the blow knocked me out for a short while.

When I opened my eyes, everything was a gray-yellow blur. My side ached. My right elbow throbbed with pain.

I tried the elbow. It seemed to move okay.

I sat up. The haze slowly began to lift, like a curtain slowly rising.

Where was I?

A sour smell invaded my nostrils. The smell of decay. Of ancient dust. Of death.

The flashlight had landed beside me on the concrete floor. I followed its beam of light toward the wall.

And gasped.

The light stopped on a hand.

A human hand.

Or was it?

The hand was attached to an arm. The arm hung stiffly from an erect body.

My hand trembling, I grabbed up the flashlight and tried to steady the light on the figure.

It was a mummy, I realized. Standing on its feet near the far wall.

Eyeless, mouthless, the bandaged face seemed to stare back at me, tense and ready, as if waiting for me to make the first move.

13

A mummy?

The light darted over its featureless face. I couldn't steady my hand. My whole body was shaking.

Frozen in place, not able to move off the hard floor, I gaped at the frightening figure. I suddenly realized I was panting loudly.

Trying to calm myself, I sucked in a deep breath of the putrid air, and held it.

The mummy stared blindly back at me.

It stood stiffly, its arms hanging at its sides.

Why is it standing there like that? I wondered, taking another deep breath.

The ancient Egyptians didn't leave their mummies standing at attention.

Realizing that it wasn't moving forward to attack me, I began to feel a little calmer.

"Easy, Gabe. Easy," I said aloud, trying to steady the flashlight I gripped so tightly in my hand.

I coughed. The air was so foul. So *old*.

Groaning from the pain in my side, I climbed to my feet and began rapidly shining the light back and forth beyond the silent, faceless mummy.

I was in an enormous, high-ceilinged chamber. Much bigger than the chamber Uncle Ben's workers had been digging in.

And much more cluttered.

"Wow." I uttered a low cry as the pale light of the flashlight revealed an amazing scene. Dark, bandaged figures hovered all around me.

The vast chamber was *crammed* with mummies!

In the unsteady light, their shadows seemed to reach toward me.

Shuddering, I took a step back. I moved the light slowly over the strange, hideous scene.

The light burned through the shadows, revealing bandaged arms, torsos, legs, covered faces.

There were so many of them.

There were mummies leaning against the wall. Mummies lying on stone slabs, arms crossed over their chests. Mummies leaning at odd angles, crouched low or standing tall, their arms straight out in front of them like Frankenstein monsters.

Against one wall stood a row of mummy cases, their lids propped open. I turned, following the arc of my light. I realized that my fall had dropped me into the center of the room.

Behind me, I could make out an amazing array

219

of equipment. Strange, pronglike tools I had never seen before. Tall stacks of cloth. Gigantic clay pots and jars.

Easy, Gabe. Easy.

Whoa. Breathe slowly.

I took a few reluctant steps closer, trying to hold the flashlight steady.

A few more steps.

I walked up to one of the tall stacks of cloth. Linen, most likely. The material used for making mummies.

Gathering my courage, I examined some of the tools. Not touching anything. Just staring at them in the wavering light of the flashlight.

Mummy-making tools. Ancient mummy-making tools.

I stepped away. Turned back toward the crowd of unmoving figures.

My light traveled across the room and came to rest on a dark square area on the floor. Curious, I moved closer, stepping around twin mummies, lying on their backs, their arms crossed over their chests.

Whoa. Easy, Gabe.

My sneakers scraped noisily along the floor as I made my way hesitantly across the vast chamber.

The dark square on the floor was nearly the size of a swimming pool. I bent down at its edge to examine it more closely.

The surface was soft and sticky. Like tar.

Was this an ancient tar pit? Was this tar used in the making of the mummies that hovered so menacingly around the room?

I had a sudden chill that froze me to the spot.

How could this tar pit be soft after *four thousand years*?

Why was everything in this chamber — the tools, the mummies, the linen — preserved so well?

And why were these mummies — at least two dozen of them — left out like this, scattered about the room in such strange positions?

I realized that I had made an incredible discovery here. By falling through the floor, I had found a hidden chamber, a chamber where mummies had been made. I had found all of the tools and all of the materials used to make mummies four thousand years ago.

Once again, the sour smell invaded my nose. I held my breath to keep myself from gagging. It was the smell of four-thousand-year-old bodies, I realized. A smell that had been bottled up in this ancient, hidden chamber — until now.

Staring at the twisted, shadowy figures gazing back at me in faceless horror, I reached for the beeper.

Uncle Ben, you must come quickly, I thought.

I don't want to be alone down here any longer.

You must come here *now*!

I pulled the beeper off my belt and brought it up close to the light.

All I had to do, I realized, was push the button, and Uncle Ben and Sari would come running.

Gripping the small square tightly in my hand, I moved my hand to the button — and cried out in alarm.

The beeper was ruined. Wrecked. Smashed.

The button wouldn't even push.

I must have landed on it when I fell.

It was useless.

I was all alone down here.

Alone with the ancient mummies, staring facelessly, silently, at me through the deep, dark shadows.

14

All alone.

I stared in horror at the worthless beeper.

The flashlight trembled in my hand.

Suddenly, everything seemed to move in on me.
The walls. The ceiling. The darkness.

The mummies.

"Huh?"

I stumbled back a step. Then another.

I realized I was gripping the flashlight so
tightly, my hand hurt.

The light played over the faceless figures.

They weren't moving.

Of *course* they weren't moving.

I took another step back. The sour odor seemed
to grow stronger, thicker. I held my breath, but
the smell was in my nostrils, in my mouth. I could
taste it, taste the decay, taste the four-thousand-
year-old aroma of death.

I tossed the worthless beeper on the floor and

took another step back, keeping my eyes on the hovering mummies.

What was I going to do?

The smell was making me sick. I had to get out of there, had to call Uncle Ben.

Another step back.

"Help!"

I tried to shout, but my voice sounded weak, muffled by the heavy, foul air.

"Help! Can anybody hear me?" A little louder.

Tucking the flashlight under my arm, I cupped my hands around my mouth to form a megaphone. *"Can anybody hear me?"* I screamed.

I listened, desperate for a reply.

Silence.

Where *were* Sari and Uncle Ben? Why couldn't they hear me? Why weren't they looking for me?

"Help! Somebody — please help!"

I screamed as loud as I could, tilting my head up to the hole in the ceiling, the hole I had fallen through.

"Can't anybody hear me?" I shrieked.

I could feel the panic grip my chest, freeze my legs.

The panic swept over me, wave after paralyzing wave.

"Help me! *Somebody* — please!"

I took another step back.

And something crunched under my sneaker.

I uttered a high-pitched yelp and stumbled forward.

Whatever it was slithered away.

I exhaled loudly, a long sigh of relief.

And then I felt something brush against my ankle.

I cried out, and the flashlight dropped from under my arm. It clattered noisily to the floor.

The light went out.

Again, something scraped silently against me. Something hard.

I heard soft, scrabbling sounds down on the floor. Something snapped at my ankle.

I kicked hard, but hit only air.

"Ohh, help!"

There were creatures down there. A lot of them.

But what *were* they?

Again, something slapped at my ankle, and I kicked wildly.

Frantically, I bent down, grabbing for the flashlight in the darkness.

And touched something hard and warm.

"Ohh, no!"

I jerked my hand up with a startled cry.

In the darkness, groping for the flashlight, I had the feeling that the entire floor had come to life. The floor was moving in waves, rolling and tossing, seething beneath me.

Finally, I found the flashlight. I grabbed it up in my trembling hand, climbed to my feet, and struggled to turn it back on.

As I stepped backward, something slid against my leg.

It felt hard. And prickly.

I heard clicking sounds. Snapping. Creatures bumping into each other.

Panting loudly, my chest heaving, my entire body gripped with terror, I jumped up, tried to dance away as I fiddled with the flashlight.

Something crunched loudly beneath my sneaker. I danced away, hopping over something that scuttled through my legs.

Finally, the light flickered on.

My heart thudding, I lowered the yellow beam of light to the floor.

And saw the scrabbling, snapping creatures.

Scorpions!

I had stumbled into a disgusting nest of them.

"Ohh — help!"

I didn't recognize my tiny, frightened voice as I cried out. I didn't even realize I had cried out.

The light darted over the slithering creatures, their tails raised as if ready to attack, their claws snapping silently as they moved. Crawling over each other. Slithering past my ankles.

"Somebody — help!"

I leapt backwards as a pair of claws grabbed at the leg of my jeans — into another of the creatures whose tail snapped against the back of my sneaker.

Struggling to escape from the poisonous creatures, I tripped.

"No! *Please — no!*"

I couldn't save myself.

I started to fall.

My hands shot out, but there was nothing to grab on to.

I was going to plunge right into the middle of them.

"*Nooooo!*"

I uttered a frantic cry as I toppled forward.

And felt two hands grab me by the shoulders from behind.

15

A mummy! I thought.

My entire body convulsed with fear.

The scorpions snapped and scrabbled at my feet.

The strong hands gripped my shoulders, pulled me hard.

The ancient, bandaged hands.

I couldn't breathe. I couldn't think.

Finally, I managed to spin around.

"Sari!" I cried.

She gave me one more tug. We both stumbled backwards, claws snapping up at us.

"Sari — how — ?"

We moved together now, making our way toward the center of the vast chamber.

Safe. Safe from the disgusting nest of snapping scorpions.

"Saved your life," she whispered. "Yuck. Those are gross!"

"Tell me about it," I said weakly. I could still

feel the hideous creatures sliding along my ankles, still feel them slithering between my legs, crunching under my sneakers.

I don't think I'll ever forget that crunching sound.

"What are you *doing* down here?" Sari cried impatiently, as if scolding a child. "Daddy and I have been looking everywhere for you."

I pulled her even farther from the scorpions, into the center of the chamber. "How did you get down here?" I cried, struggling to calm my breathing, struggling to stop the pounding in my chest.

She pointed with her flashlight to a tunnel in the corner that I hadn't seen. "I was searching for you. Daddy and I got separated. Do you believe it? He stopped to talk to a worker, and I didn't realize it. By the time I turned back, he was gone. Then I saw the light moving around in here. I thought it was Daddy."

"You got lost, too?" I asked, wiping beads of cold sweat off my forehead with the back of my hand.

"I'm not lost. *You're* lost," she insisted. "How could you *do* that, Gabe? Daddy and I were totally freaked."

"Why didn't you wait up for me?" I demanded angrily. "I called to you. You just disappeared."

"We didn't hear you," she replied, shaking her head. I was really glad to see her. But I hated the way she was looking at me, like I was some

229

kind of hopeless idiot. "I guess we got involved in our argument. We thought you were right behind us. Then when we turned around, you were gone." She sighed and shook her head. "What a day!"

"What a day?" I cried shrilly. "What a day?"

"Gabe, why did you *do* that?" she demanded. "You know we were supposed to stay close together."

"Hey — it wasn't my fault," I insisted angrily.

"Daddy is so mad," Sari said, shining her light in my face.

I raised my arm to shield my eyes. "Cut it out," I snapped. "He won't be mad when he sees what I've discovered. Look."

I shined my light onto a mummy crouching near the tar pit, then moved it to another mummy, this one lying down, then to the row of mummy cases against the wall.

"Wow." Sari mouthed the word silently. Her eyes grew wide with surprise.

"Yeah. Wow," I said, starting to feel a little more like normal. "The chamber is filled with mummies. And there are all kinds of tools and cloth and everything you need to make a mummy. It's all in perfect shape, like it hasn't been touched in thousands of years." I couldn't hide my excitement. "And I discovered it all," I added.

"This must be where they prepared the mummies for burial," Sari said, her eyes darting from mummy to mummy. "But why are some of them standing up like that?"

I shrugged. "Beats me."

She walked over to admire the stacks of neatly folded linen. "Wow. This is amazing, Gabe."

"Outstanding!" I agreed. "And if I hadn't stopped to tie my sneaker, I never would have discovered it."

"You're going to be famous," Sari said, a smile spreading across her face. "Thanks to *me* saving your life."

"Sari — " I started.

But she had moved across the room and was admiring one of the upright mummies close up. "Wait till Daddy sees all this," she said, suddenly sounding as excited as me.

"We have to call him," I said eagerly. I glanced back at the scorpion nest and felt a chill of fear tighten the back of my neck.

"People were so tiny back then," she said, holding her flashlight up close to the mummy's covered face. "Look — I'm taller than this one."

"Sari, use your beeper," I said impatiently, walking over to her.

"Yuck. There are bugs crawling in this one's face," she said, stepping back and lowering the light. She made a disgusted face. "Gross."

"Come on. Use your beeper. Call Uncle Ben," I said. I reached for the beeper at her waist, but she pulled away.

"Okay, okay. Why didn't you use *yours*?" She eyed me suspiciously. "You forgot about it, didn't you, Gabe!" she accused.

"No way," I replied sharply. "Mine broke when I fell into this place."

She made a face and pulled the beeper off her belt loop. I shined my light on it as she pushed the button. She pressed it twice, just to make sure, then clipped it back onto her jeans.

We stood with our arms crossed, waiting for Uncle Ben to follow the radio signals and find us.

"It shouldn't take him long," Sari said, her eyes on the tunnel in the corner. "He wasn't far behind me."

Sure enough, a few seconds later, we heard the sounds of someone approaching in the tunnel.

"Uncle Ben!" I called excitedly. "Look what I've found!"

Sari and I both started to run to the tunnel, our lights zigzagging over the low entrance.

"Daddy, you won't believe — " Sari started.

She stopped when the stooped figure leaned out of the darkness and straightened up.

We both gaped in horror, our flashlights making his mustached face glow eerily.

"It's Ahmed!" Sari cried, grabbing my arm.

16

I swallowed hard.

Sari and I stared at each other. I saw her features tighten in fear.

Ahmed.

He had tried to kidnap us. And now he had us all alone down here.

He stepped forward, a flaming torch held high in one hand. His black hair glowed in the flickering flames. His eyes narrowed at us in menace.

"Ahmed, what are you doing here?" Sari called, grasping my arm so hard, I winced.

"What are *you* doing here?" he asked softly, his voice as cold as his eyes.

Holding the torch in front of him, he stepped into the chamber. His eyes went around the room, as if inspecting it, making sure that nothing had been moved.

"My dad will be here in a second," Sari warned him. "I just beeped him."

"I tried to warn your father," Ahmed said, star-

233

ing hard at Sari. The flickering orange light from the torch made him grow bright, then fade into shadow.

"Warn him?" Sari asked.

"About the curse," Ahmed said without emotion.

"Uncle Ben mentioned some kind of curse to me," I said, glancing nervously at Sari. "I don't think he takes that kind of thing seriously."

"He should!" Ahmed replied, screaming the words, his eyes glowing with anger in the torch light.

Sari and I stared back at him in silence.

Where is Uncle Ben? I wondered.

What's keeping him?

Hurry, I urged silently. *Please — hurry!*

"The curse must be carried out," Ahmed said softly again, almost sadly. "I have no choice. You have violated the priestess's chamber."

"Priestess?" I stammered.

Sari was still squeezing my arm. I tugged it away. She crossed her arms resolutely over her chest.

"This chamber belongs to the Priestess Khala," Ahmed said, lowering the torch. "This is the sacred Preparation Chamber of the Priestess Khala, and you have violated it."

"Well, we didn't know," Sari snapped. "I really don't see what's the big deal, Ahmed."

"She's right," I said quickly. "We didn't touch

anything. We didn't move anything. I don't think — "

"*Shut up, you fools!*" Ahmed screamed. He swung the torch angrily as if trying to hit us.

"Ahmed, my dad will be here any second," Sari repeated, her voice trembling.

We both turned our eyes to the tunnel. It was dark and silent.

No sign of Uncle Ben.

"Your father is a smart man," Ahmed said. "It is too bad he wasn't smart enough to heed my warnings."

"Warnings?" Sari asked.

I realized she was stalling for time, trying to keep Ahmed talking until Uncle Ben arrived.

"I frightened the two workers," Ahmed confessed to Sari. "I frightened them to show your father that the curse was alive, that I was prepared to carry out Khala's wishes."

"How did you frighten them?" Sari demanded.

He smiled. "I gave them a little demonstration. I showed them what it might feel like to be boiled alive." He turned his eyes to the tar pit. "They didn't like it," he added quietly.

"But, Ahmed — " Sari started.

He cut her off. "Your father should have known better than to return here. He should have believed me. He should have believed in the Priestess's curse. The Priestess cursed all who would violate her chamber."

"But, come on, you don't really believe — " I started.

He raised the torch menacingly. "It was decreed by Khala more than four thousand years ago that this sacred chamber would not be violated," he cried, gesturing with the torch, leaving a trail of orange light against the darkness. "Since that time, from generation to generation, descendants of Khala have made sure that the Priestess's command was obeyed."

"But, Ahmed — " Sari cried.

"It has come to me," he continued, ignoring her, ignoring us both, staring at the ceiling as he spoke, as if speaking directly to the Priestess up in the heavens. "It has come to me as a descendant of Khala to make sure the curse is carried out."

I stared past Ahmed to the tunnel. Still no sign of Uncle Ben.

Was he coming? Had Sari's beeper worked? What was keeping him?

"I volunteered to work for your father to make sure that Khala's sacred sanctuary was not violated," Ahmed continued, shadows flickering over his menacing face. "When he would not heed my warnings, I had to take action. I frightened the two workers. Then I planned to take you away, to hide you until he agreed to stop his work."

He lowered the torch. His face filled with sadness. "Now, I have no choice. I must carry out

236

my sacred duties. I must keep the ancient promise to Khala."

"But what does that *mean?*" Sari cried. The orange torchlight revealed her frightened expression.

"What does it mean?" Ahmed repeated. He gestured with the torch. "Look around you."

We both turned and glanced quickly around the chamber. But we didn't understand.

"The mummies," he explained.

We still didn't understand. "What about the mummies?" I managed to stammer.

"They were all violators of the Priestess's chamber," Ahmed revealed. The thin smile that formed on his face could only be described as a proud smile.

"You mean — they're not from ancient Egypt?" Sari cried, raising her hands in horror to her face.

"A few of them," Ahmed replied, still smiling that frightening, cold smile. "A few of them were ancient intruders. Some are quite recent. But they all have one thing in common. They all became victims of the curse. And they all were mummified *alive!*"

"No!" I screamed without realizing it.

Ahmed ignored my terrified outburst. "I did that one myself," he said, pointing to a mummy standing stiffly at attention at the edge of the tar pit.

"Oh, how awful!" Sari cried, her voice trembling.

I stared hopefully at the tunnel opening behind Ahmed. But there was still no sign of Uncle Ben.

"Today, I must go to work again," Ahmed announced. Today there will be new mummies. New trophies for Khala."

"You can't *do* that!" Sari shrieked.

I grabbed her hand.

To my horror, I understood perfectly now. I understood why some of the mummies were in such good condition.

They were new.

All of the tools, the tar, the linen — they had been used by descendants of Khala, descendants like Ahmed. Since the time of Khala, anyone who had entered the chamber — the chamber we were now standing in — had been mummified.

Alive.

And now Sari and I were about to become mummies, too.

"Ahmed, you *can't!*" Sari cried. She let go of my hand and balled her hands into angry fists at her side.

"It is the will of Khala," he replied softly, his dark eyes glowing in the light of the torch.

I saw a long-bladed dagger appear in his free hand. The blade caught the light from the torch.

Sari and I both took a step back as Ahmed began moving toward us with quick, determined strides.

17

As Ahmed approached, Sari and I shrank back to the center of the chamber.

Run, I thought.

We can run away from him.

My eyes searched frantically for a place we could escape through.

But there was no way out.

The tunnel in the corner appeared to be the only opening. And we'd have to run right past Ahmed to get to it.

Sari, I saw, was frantically pressing the beeper at her waist. She glanced at me, her features tight with fear.

"Yowwww!"

I cried out as I suddenly backed into someone.

I turned and stared into the bandaged face of a mummy.

With a loud gasp, I lurched away from it.

"Let's make a run for the tunnel," I whispered

239

to Sari, my throat so dry and tight, I could barely make myself heard. "He can't get both of us."

Sari stared back at me, confused. I don't know if she heard me or not.

"There is no escape," Ahmed said softly, as if reading my thoughts. "There is no escape from Khala's curse."

"He — he's going to *kill* us!" Sari screamed.

"You have violated her sacred chamber," Ahmed said, raising the torch high, holding the dagger at his waist.

He stepped nearer. "I saw you yesterday climb into the sacred sarcophagus. I saw you two *playing* in Khala's holy chamber. It was then that I knew I had to carry out my sacred duties. I — "

Sari and I both cried out as something dropped from the chamber ceiling.

All three of us looked up to see a rope ladder dangling from the hole I had fallen through. It swung back and forth as it was lowered, nearly to the floor.

"Are you down there? I'm coming down!" Uncle Ben shouted down to us.

"Uncle Ben — no!" I screamed.

But he was already moving down the ladder, making his way quickly, the ladder steadying under his weight.

Halfway down, he stopped and peered into the chamber. "What on earth — ?" he cried, his eyes roaming over the amazing scene.

And then he saw Ahmed.

"Ahmed, what are *you* doing here?" Uncle Ben cried in surprise. He quickly lowered himself to the floor, jumping down the last three rungs.

"Merely carrying out Khala's wishes," Ahmed said, his face expressionless now, his eyes narrowed in anticipation.

"Khala? The Priestess?" Uncle Ben wrinkled his features in confusion.

"He's going to kill us!" Sari cried, rushing up to her dad, throwing her arms around his waist. "Daddy — he's going to kill us! And then turn us into *mummies!*"

Uncle Ben held Sari and looked over her shoulder accusingly at Ahmed. "Is this true?"

"The chamber has been violated. It has fallen to me, Doctor, to carry out the curse."

Uncle Ben put his hands on Sari's trembling shoulders and gently moved her aside. Then he began to make his way slowly, steadily, toward Ahmed.

"Ahmed, let us go out of here and discuss this," he said, raising his right hand as if offering it in friendship.

Ahmed took a step back, raising the torch menacingly. "The Priestess's will must not be ignored."

"Ahmed, you are a scientist, and so am I," Uncle Ben said. I couldn't believe how calm he sounded. I wondered if it was an act.

241

The scene was tense. We were in such terrifying danger.

But I felt just a little bit calmer knowing that my uncle was here, knowing that he'd be able to handle Ahmed and get us out of here — alive.

I glanced reassuringly at Sari, who was staring hard, biting her lower lip in tense concentration as her father approached Ahmed.

"Ahmed, put down the torch," Uncle Ben urged, his hand extended. "The dagger, too. Please. Let's discuss this, scientist to scientist."

"What is there to discuss?" Ahmed asked softly, his eyes studying Uncle Ben intently. "The will of Khala must be carried out, as it has been for four thousand years. That cannot be discussed."

"As scientist to scientist," Uncle Ben repeated, returning Ahmed's stare as if challenging him. "The curse is ancient. Khala has had her way for many centuries. Perhaps it is time to let it rest. Lower your weapons, Ahmed. Let's talk about this. Scientist to scientist."

It's going to be okay, I thought, breathing a long sigh of relief. It's all going to be okay. We're going to get out of here.

But then Ahmed moved with startling quickness.

Without warning, without a word, he pulled back his arms and, gripping the torch handle with both hands, swung it as hard as he could at Uncle Ben's head.

The torch made a loud *thonk* as it connected with the side of Uncle Ben's face.

The orange flames danced up.

A swirl of bright color.

And then shadows.

Uncle Ben groaned. His eyes bulged wide with surprise.

With pain.

The torch hadn't set him aflame. But the blow knocked him out.

He slumped to his knees. Then his eyes closed, and he dropped limply to the floor.

Ahmed raised the torch high, his eyes gleaming with excitement, with triumph.

And I knew we were doomed.

18

"Daddy!"

Sari rushed to her father and knelt at his side.

But Ahmed moved quickly, thrusting the torch toward her, holding the dagger ready, forcing her to back away.

A thin trickle of blood, glowing darkly in the light of the fire, rolled down the side of Uncle Ben's face. He groaned, but didn't stir.

I glanced quickly at the mummies scattered around the room. It was hard to believe that we would soon be one of them.

I thought of leaping at Ahmed, trying to knock him over. I imagined grabbing the torch, swinging it at him, forcing him against the wall. Forcing him to let us escape.

But the blade of the dagger glowed, as if warning me to stay back.

I'm just a kid, I thought.

Thinking I could beat a grown man with a knife and a torch was just crazy.

Crazy.

The whole scene was crazy. And terrifying.

I suddenly felt sick. My stomach tightened, and a wave of nausea swept over me.

"Let us go — *now!*" Sari screamed at Ahmed.

To my surprise, he reacted by swinging back the torch and heaving it across the room.

It landed with a soft *plop* in the center of the tar pit. Instantly, the surface of the tar burst into flames. The flames spread, leaping up toward the chamber ceiling, until the entire square was aflame.

As I stared in amazement, the tar popped and bubbled beneath the orange and red covering of flames.

"We must wait for it to boil," Ahmed said calmly, the shadows cast by the flames flickering across his face and clothing.

The chamber grew thick with smoke. Sari and I both started to cough.

Ahmed bent down and put his hands under Uncle Ben's shoulders. He began to drag him across the floor.

"Leave him alone!" Sari screamed, running frantically toward Ahmed.

I saw that she was going to try to fight him.

I grabbed her shoulders and held her back.

We were no match for Ahmed. He had already knocked Uncle Ben unconscious. There was no telling what he would do to us.

Holding onto Sari, I stared at him. What did he plan to do now?

It didn't take long to find out.

With surprising strength, he pulled Uncle Ben across the floor to one of the open mummy cases against the wall. Then he hoisted him over the side and shoved him into the case. Not even the slightest bit out of breath, Ahmed slid the lid closed over my unconscious uncle.

Then he turned to us. "You two — into that one." He pointed to an enormous mummy case on a tall pedestal next to Uncle Ben's. It was nearly as tall as I was, and at least ten feet long. It must have been built to hold a mummified person — and all of his or her possessions.

"Let us go!" Sari insisted. "Let us out of here. We won't tell anyone what happened. Really!"

"Please climb into the case," Ahmed insisted patiently. "We must wait for the tar to be ready."

"We're not going in there," I said.

I was shaking all over. I could feel the blood pulsing at my temples. I didn't even realize I was saying what I was saying. I was so scared, I didn't even hear myself.

I glanced at Sari. She stood defiantly with her arms crossed tightly over her chest. But despite her brave pose, I could see her chin trembling and her eyes beginning to tear.

"Into the coffin," Ahmed repeated, "to await your fate. Khala will not be kept waiting. The ancient curse will be carried out in her name."

"No!" I cried angrily.

I stood on tiptoe and peered into the enormous mummy case. It smelled so sour in there, I nearly hurled.

The case was made of wood. It was warped and stained and peeling inside. In the flickering light, I was sure I saw dozens of insects crawling around in there.

"Get into the case *now*!" Ahmed demanded.

19

Sari climbed up over the side and lowered herself into the ancient mummy case. She always had to be first at everything. But this was one time I didn't mind.

I hesitated, resting my hand on the rotting wood on the side of the case. I glanced at the case next to it, the case with Uncle Ben inside. It was carved of stone, and the heavy stone lid was closed, sealing it up tight.

Did Uncle Ben have any air in there? I wondered, gripped with fear. Was he able to breathe?

And, then, I thought glumly, what difference does it make? All three of us are going to be dead soon. All three of us are going to be mummies, locked away in this hidden chamber forever.

"Get in — now!" Ahmed ordered, his dark eyes burning into mine.

"I — I'm just a *kid*!" I cried. I don't know where the words came from. I was so scared, I really didn't know what I was saying.

An unpleasant sneer formed on Ahmed's face. "Many of the pharaohs were your age at death," he said.

I wanted to keep him talking. I had the desperate idea that if I could keep the conversation going, I could get us out of this mess.

But I couldn't think of anything to say. My brain just froze.

"Get in," Ahmed ordered, moving toward me menacingly.

Feeling totally defeated, I slid one leg over the side of the rotting coffin, raised myself up, and then dropped down beside Sari.

She had her head bowed, and her eyes shut tight. I think she was praying. She didn't glance up, even when I touched her shoulder.

The coffin lid began to slide over us. The last thing I saw were the red flames leaping up over the pit of tar. Then the lid closed us into complete blackness.

"Gabe . . ." Sari whispered a few seconds after the lid was closed. "I'm frightened."

For some reason, her confession made me snicker. She said it with such *surprise*. As if being frightened was a startling new experience.

"I'm too frightened to be frightened," I whispered back.

She grabbed my hand and squeezed it. Her hand was even colder and clammier than mine.

"He's crazy," she whispered.

"Yeah. I know," I replied, still holding onto her hand.

"I think there are bugs in here," she said with a shudder. "I can feel them crawling on me."

"Me, too," I told her. I realized I was gritting my teeth. I always do that when I'm nervous. And now I was more nervous than I thought was humanly possible.

"Poor Daddy," Sari said.

The air in the coffin was already beginning to feel stuffy and hot. I tried to ignore the disgusting sour smell, but it had crept into my nostrils, and I could even taste it. I held my breath to keep from gagging.

"We're going to suffocate in here," I said glumly.

"He's going to kill us before we can suffocate," Sari wailed. "Ow!" I could hear her slap at a bug on her arm.

"Maybe something will happen," I told her. Pretty lame. But I couldn't think of what else to say. I couldn't *think*. Period.

"All I keep thinking about is how he's going to reach in and pull my brain out through my nose," Sari wailed. "Why did you have to tell me that, Gabe?"

It took me a while to reply. Then, all I could say was, "Sorry." I began to picture the same thing, and another wave of nausea swept over me.

"We can't just sit here," I said. "We have to

escape." I tried to ignore the thick, sour smell.

"Huh? How?"

"Let's try to push up the lid," I said. "Maybe if we both push together . . ."

I counted to three in a low whisper, and we both flattened our hands against the coffin top and pushed up as hard as we could.

No. The lid wouldn't budge.

"Maybe he's locked it or put something heavy on top of it," Sari suggested with a miserable sigh.

"Maybe," I replied, feeling just as miserable.

We sat in silence for a while. I could hear Sari breathing. She was sort of sobbing as she breathed. I realized my heart was racing. I could feel my temples throbbing.

I pictured the long hook that Ahmed would use to pull our brains out of our heads. I tried to force the thought out of my mind, but it wouldn't go away.

I remembered being a mummy two Halloweens ago, and how the costume unraveled in front of my friends.

Little did I know then that I'd soon have a mummy costume that would *never* unravel.

Time passed. I don't know how long.

I realized I had been sitting with my legs crossed. Now they were beginning to fall asleep. I uncrossed them and stretched them out. The mummy case was so big, Sari and I could both lie down if we wanted to.

But we were too tense and terrified to lie down.

I was the first to hear the scrabbling sound. Like something climbing quickly around inside the mummy case.

At first I thought it was Sari. But she grabbed my hand with her icy hand, and I realized she hadn't moved from in front of me.

We both listened hard.

Something near us, something right next to us, bumped the side of the case.

A mummy?

Was there a mummy in the case with us?

Moving?

I heard a soft groan.

Sari squeezed my hand so tightly, it hurt, and I uttered a sharp cry.

Another sound. Closer.

"Gabe — " Sari whispered, her voice tiny and shrill. "Gabe — there's *something* in here with us!"

20

It's not a mummy, I told myself.

It *can't* be.

It's a bug. A very large bug. Moving across the coffin floor.

It's not a mummy. It's not a mummy.

The words repeated in my mind.

I didn't have too long to think about it. Whatever it was crept closer.

"Hey!" a voice whispered.

Sari and I both shrieked.

"Where *are* you guys?"

We recognized the voice immediately.

"Uncle Ben!" I cried, swallowing hard, my heart pounding.

"Daddy!" Sari lunged over me to get to her father.

"But how?" I stammered. "How did you get in here?"

"Easy," he replied, squeezing my shoulder reassuringly.

"Daddy — I don't *believe* it!" Sari wailed. I couldn't see in the blackness of the closed coffin, but I think she was crying.

"I'm okay. I'm okay," he repeated several times, trying to calm her down.

"How did you get out of that case and into this one?" I asked, totally confused and amazed.

"There's an escape hatch," Uncle Ben explained. "A small opening with a doorway. The Egyptians built hidden doorways and escape hatches into many of their mummy cases. For the corpse's soul to be able to leave."

"Wow," I said. I didn't know *what* to say.

"Ahmed is so caught up in his ancient curse mumbo jumbo, he's forgotten about this little detail," Uncle Ben said. I felt his hand on my shoulder again. "Come on, you two. Follow me."

"But he's out there — " I started.

"No," Uncle Ben replied quickly. "He's slipped away. When I climbed out of my case, I looked for him. I didn't see him anywhere. Maybe he went somewhere else while he's waiting for the tar to get hot enough. Or maybe he decided to just leave us in the mummy cases to suffocate."

I felt a bug slither up my leg. I slapped at it, then tried to pull it out from inside the leg of my jeans.

"Out we go," Uncle Ben said.

I heard him groan as he turned in the enormous

coffin. Then I could hear him crawling to the back.

I saw a small rectangle of light as he pushed open the hidden door in the back of the case. It was a very small escape hatch, just big enough for us to squeeze through.

I followed Uncle Ben and Sari out of the case, flattening myself to crawl out the small opening, then dropping onto all fours on the chamber floor.

It took a while for my eyes to adjust to the brightness.

The red flames still danced over the pit of bubbling tar, casting eerie blue shadows on all four chamber walls. The mummies stood as before, frozen in place around the room, shadows flickering over their faceless forms.

As my eyes began to focus, I saw that Uncle Ben had an enormous, dark bruise on the side of his head. A wide ribbon of dried blood streaked down his cheek.

"Let's get out of here before Ahmed comes back," he whispered, standing between us, one hand on each of our shoulders.

Sari looked pale and trembly. Her lower lip was bleeding from her chewing on it so hard.

Uncle Ben started toward the rope ladder in the center of the chamber, but then stopped. "It'll take too long," he said, thinking out loud. "Come on. To the tunnel. Hurry."

All three of us started jogging toward the tunnel in the corner. Looking down, I saw that my stupid shoelace had come untied again. But there was *no way* I was going to stop to tie it!

We were about to get *out* of there!

A few seconds before, I had given up all hope. But now, here we were out of the mummy case and heading to freedom.

We were just a few yards in front of the tunnel entrance when the tunnel suddenly filled with orange light.

Then, from out of the tunnel, Ahmed emerged, holding a new torch in front of him, the flames revealing a startled look on his face.

"No!" Sari and I cried in unison.

All three of us skidded to a halt right in front of him.

"You cannot escape!" Ahmed said softly, quickly regaining his composure, his startled expression tightening to anger. "You *will not* escape!"

He thrust the torch toward Uncle Ben, who was forced to fall backwards, out of reach of the hissing flames. He landed hard on his elbows and cried out in pain.

His cry brought a grim smile to Ahmed's lips. "You have made Khala angry," he announced, raising the torch above his head and reaching for the dagger sheathed at his waist. "You will not join the other violators of this chamber."

Whew. I breathed a sigh of relief.

Ahmed had changed his mind. He wasn't going to turn us into mummies after all.

"The three of you will die in the tar pit," he declared.

Sari and I exchanged horrified glances. Uncle Ben had climbed back to his feet and put his arms around us. "Ahmed, can't we talk about this calmly and rationally as scientists?" he asked.

"To the tar pit," Ahmed ordered, thrusting the flaming torch angrily at us.

"Ahmed — *please!*" Uncle Ben cried in a whining, frightened tone I'd never heard from him before.

Ahmed ignored Uncle Ben's desperate pleas. Pushing the torch at our backs and gesturing with the long-bladed dagger, he forced us to make our way to the edge of the pit.

The tar was bubbling noisily now, making ugly popping and sucking sounds. The flames across the top were low and red.

I tried to pull back. It smelled so bad. And the steam coming off it was so hot, it made my face burn.

"One by one, you will jump," Ahmed said.

He was standing a few feet behind us as we stared down into the bubbling tar. "If you don't jump, I will be forced to push you."

"Ahmed — " Uncle Ben began. But Ahmed brushed the torch against Ben's back.

"It has come to me," Ahmed said solemnly. "The

257

honor of carrying out Khala's wishes."

The tar fumes were so overwhelming, I thought I was going to faint. The pit started to tilt in front of me. I felt very dizzy.

I shoved my hands into my jeans pockets, to steady myself, I guess. And my hand closed around something I had forgotten about.

The Summoner.

The mummy hand that I carry around everywhere.

I'm not sure why — I wasn't thinking clearly, if at all — but I pulled out the little mummy hand.

I spun around quickly. And I held the mummy hand up high.

I can't really explain what was going through my mind. I was so terrified, so overwhelmed with fear, that I was thinking a hundred things at once.

Maybe I thought the mummy hand would distract Ahmed.

Or interest him.

Or confuse him.

Or frighten him.

Maybe I was just stalling for time.

Or maybe I was unconsciously remembering the legend behind the hand that the kid at the garage sale had told me.

The legend of why it was called The Summoner.

How it was used to call up ancient souls and spirits.

Or maybe I wasn't thinking anything at all.

But I spun around and, gripping it by its slender wrist, held the mummy hand up high.

And waited.

Ahmed stared at it.

But nothing happened.

21

I waited, standing there like the Statue of Liberty with the little hand raised high above my head.

It seemed as if I were standing like that for hours.

Sari and Uncle Ben stared at the hand.

Lowering the torch a few inches, Ahmed squinted at the mummy hand. Then his eyes grew wider, and his mouth dropped open in surprise.

He cried out. I couldn't understand what he was saying. The words were in a language I'd never heard. Ancient Egyptian, maybe.

He took a step back, his surprised expression quickly replaced by a wide-eyed look of fear.

"The hand of the Priestess!" he cried.

At least, that's what I *think* he cried — because I was suddenly distracted by what was going on behind him.

Sari uttered a low cry.

All three of us stared over Ahmed's shoulder in disbelief.

A mummy propped against the wall appeared to lean forward.

Another mummy, lying on its back, slowly sat up, creaking as it raised itself.

"No!" I cried, still holding the mummy hand high.

Sari and Uncle Ben were gaping wide-eyed as the vast chamber filled with motion. As the mummies creaked and groaned to life.

The air filled with the odor of ancient dust, of decay.

In the shadowy light, I saw one mummy, then another, straighten up, stand tall. They stretched their bandaged arms above their featureless heads. Slowly. Painfully.

Staggering, moving stiffly, the mummies lumbered forward.

I watched, frozen in amazement, as they climbed out of mummy cases, raised themselves from the floor, leaned forward, took their first slow, heavy steps, their muscles groaning, dust rising up from their dry, dead bodies.

They're dead, I thought.

All of them. Dead. Dead for so many years.

But now they were rising up, climbing from their ancient coffins, struggling toward us on their heavy, dead legs.

Their bandaged feet scraped across the chamber floor as they gathered in a group.

Scrape. Scrape. Scrape.

A dry, shuffling sound I knew I'd never forget. *Scrape. Scrape.*

The faceless army approached. Bandaged arms outstretched, they lumbered toward us, creaking and groaning. Moaning softly with ancient pain.

Ahmed caught the astonishment on our faces and spun around.

He cried out again in that strange language as he saw the mummies advancing on us, scraping so softly, so deliberately, across the chamber floor.

And, then, with a furious scream, Ahmed heaved the torch at the mummy in the lead.

The torch hit the mummy in the chest and bounced to the floor. Flames burst from the mummy's chest, immediately spreading over the arms and down the legs.

But the mummy kept advancing, didn't slow, didn't react at all to the fire that was quickly consuming it.

Gaping in openmouthed horror, babbling an endless stream of words in that mysterious language, Ahmed tried to run.

But he was too late.

The burning mummy lunged at him. The ancient figure caught Ahmed up by the throat, lifted him high above its flaming shoulders.

Ahmed uttered a high-pitched shriek of terror as the other mummies lumbered forward. Moaning and wailing through their yellowed bandages, they moved in to help their burning colleague.

They raised Ahmed high above their moaning heads.

And then held him over the burning tar pit.

Squirming and kicking, Ahmed uttered a piercing scream as they held him over the boiling, bubbling, steaming tar.

I closed my eyes. The heat and tar fumes swirled around me. I felt as if I were being swallowed up, pulled down into the steaming blackness.

When I opened my eyes, I saw Ahmed fleeing to the tunnel, staggering clumsily, shrieking in openmouthed terror as he ran. The mummies remained by the pit, enjoying their victory.

I realized I was still holding the mummy hand over my head. I lowered it slowly, and gazed at Sari and Uncle Ben. They were standing beside me, their faces filled with confusion. And relief.

"The mummies — " I managed to utter.

"Look," Sari said, pointing.

I followed the direction of her gaze. The mummies were all back in place. Some were leaning, some propped at odd angles, some lying down.

They were exactly as they had been when I entered the chamber.

"Huh?" My eyes darted rapidly around the room.

Had they all moved? Had they raised themselves, stood up, and staggered toward us? Or had we imagined it all?

No.

We *couldn't* have imagined it.

Ahmed was gone. We were safe.

"We're okay," Uncle Ben said gratefully, throwing his arms around Sari and me. "We're okay. We're okay."

"We can go now!" Sari cried happily, hugging her dad. Then she turned to me. "You saved our lives," she said. She had to choke out the words. But she said them.

Then Uncle Ben turned his gaze on me and the object I still gripped tightly in front of me. "Thanks for the helping hand," Uncle Ben said.

We had an enormous dinner at a restaurant back in Cairo. It's a miracle any of us got any food down since we were all talking at once, chattering excitedly, reliving our adventure, trying to make sense of it all.

I was spinning The Summoner around on the table.

Uncle Ben grinned at me. "I had no idea *how* special that mummy hand was!"

He took it from me and examined it closely. "Better not play with it," he said seriously. "We must treat it carefully." He shook his head. "Some great scientist *I* am!" he exclaimed scornfully.

"When I saw it, I thought it was just a toy, some kind of reproduction. But this hand may be my biggest discovery of all!"

"It's my good luck charm," I said, handling it gently as I took it back.

"You can say *that* again!" Sari said appreciatively. The nicest thing she'd ever said to me.

Back at the hotel, I surprised myself by falling asleep instantly. I thought I'd be up for hours, thinking about all that had happened. But I guess all the excitement had exhausted me.

The next morning, Sari, Uncle Ben, and I had a big breakfast in the room. I had a plate of scrambled eggs and a bowl of Frosted Flakes. As I ate, I fiddled with the little mummy hand.

All three of us were feeling good, happy that our frightening adventure was over. We were kidding around, teasing each other, laughing a lot.

After I finished my cereal, I raised the little mummy hand high. "O, Summoner," I chanted in a deep voice, "I summon the ancient spirits. Come alive. Come alive again!"

"Stop it, Gabe," Sari snapped. She grabbed for the hand, but I swung it out of her reach.

"That isn't funny," she said. "You shouldn't fool around like that."

"Are you chicken?" I asked, laughing at her. I could see that she was really frightened, which made me enjoy my little joke even more.

Keeping it away from her, I raised the hand

high. "I summon thee, ancient spirits of the dead," I chanted. "Come to me. Come to me now!"

And there was a loud knock on the door.

All three of us gasped.

Uncle Ben knocked over his juice glass. It clattered onto the table and spilled.

I froze with the little hand in the air.

Another loud knock.

We heard a scrabbling at the door. The sound of ancient, bandaged fingers struggling with the lock.

Sari and I exchanged horrified glances.

I slowly lowered the hand as the door swung open.

Two shadowy figures lumbered into the room.

"Mom and Dad!" I cried.

I'll bet they were surprised at how glad I was to see them.

LET'S GET INVISIBLE!

1

I went invisible for the first time on my twelfth birthday.

It was all Whitey's fault, in a way. Whitey is my dog. He's just a mutt, part terrier, part everything else. He's all black, so of course we named him Whitey.

If Whitey hadn't been sniffing around in the attic . . .

Well, maybe I'd better back up a bit and start at the beginning.

My birthday was on a rainy Saturday. It was a few minutes before kids would start arriving for my birthday party, so I was getting ready.

Getting ready means brushing my hair.

My brother is always on my case about my hair. He gives me a hard time because I spend so much time in front of the mirror brushing it and checking it out.

The thing is, I just happen to have great hair. It's very thick and sort of a golden brown, and

269

just a little bit wavy. My hair is my best feature, so I like to make sure it looks okay.

Also, I have very big ears. They stick out a lot. So I have to keep making sure that my hair covers my ears. It's important.

"Max, it's messed up in the back," my brother, Lefty, said, standing behind me as I studied my hair in the front hall mirror.

His name is really Noah, but I call him Lefty because he's the only left-handed person in our family. Lefty was tossing a softball up and catching it in his left hand. He knew he wasn't supposed to toss that softball around in the house, but he always did it anyway.

Lefty is two years younger than me. He's not a bad guy, but he has too much energy. He always has to be tossing a ball around, drumming his hands on the table, hitting something, running around, falling down, leaping into things, wrestling with me. You get the idea. Dad says that Lefty has ants in his pants. It's a dumb expression, but it sort of describes my brother.

I turned and twisted my neck to see the back of my hair. "It is *not* messed up, liar," I said.

"Think fast!" Lefty shouted, and he tossed the softball at me.

I made a grab for it and missed. It hit the wall just below the mirror with a loud *thud*. Lefty and I held our breath, waiting to see if Mom heard the sound. But she didn't. I think she was in the kitchen doing something to the birthday cake.

"That was dumb," I whispered to Lefty. "You almost broke the mirror."

"*You're* dumb," he said. Typical.

"Why don't you learn to throw right-handed? Then maybe I could catch it sometimes," I told him. I liked to tease him about being left-handed because he really hated it.

"You stink," he said, picking up the softball.

I was used to it. He said it a hundred times a day. I guess he thought it was clever or something.

He's a good kid for a ten-year-old, but he doesn't have much of a vocabulary.

"Your ears are sticking out," he said.

I knew he was lying. I started to answer him, but the doorbell rang.

He and I raced down the narrow hallway to the front door. "Hey, it's *my* party!" I told him.

But Lefty got to the door first and pulled it open.

My best friend, Zack, pulled open the screen door and hurried into the house. It was starting to rain pretty hard, and he was already soaked.

He handed me a present, wrapped in silver paper, raindrops dripping off it. "It's a bunch of comic books," he said. "I already read 'em. The *X-Force* graphic novel is kind of cool."

"Thanks," I said. "They don't look too wet."

Lefty grabbed the present from my hand and

ran into the living room with it. "Don't open it!" I shouted. He said he was just starting a pile.

Zack took off his Red Sox cap, and I got a look at his new haircut. "Wow! You look . . . different," I said, studying his new look. His black hair was buzzed real short on the left side. The rest of it was long, brushed straight to the right.

"Did you invite girls?" he asked me, "or is it just boys?"

"Some girls are coming," I told him. "Erin and April. Maybe my cousin Debra." I knew he liked Debra.

He nodded thoughtfully. Zack has a real serious face. He has these little blue eyes that always look far away, like he's thinking hard about something. Like he's real deep.

He's sort of an intense guy. Not nervous. Just keyed up. And very competitive. He has to win at everything. If he comes in second place, he gets really upset and kicks the furniture. You know the kind.

"What are we going to do?" Zack asked, shaking the water off his Red Sox cap.

I shrugged. "We were supposed to be in the back yard. Dad put the volleyball net up this morning. But that was before it started to rain. I rented some movies. Maybe we'll watch them."

The doorbell rang. Lefty appeared again from out of nowhere, pushed Zack and me out of the way, and made a dive for the door. "Oh, it's you," I heard him say.

"Thanks for the welcome." I recognized Erin's squeaky voice. Some kids call Erin "Mouse" because of that voice, and because she's tiny like a mouse. She has short, straight blonde hair, and I think she's cute, but of course I'd never tell anyone that.

"Can we come in?" I recognized April's voice next. April is the other girl in our group. She has curly black hair and dark, sad eyes. I always thought she was really sad, but then I figured out that she's just shy.

"The party's tomorrow," I heard Lefty tell them.

"Huh?" Both girls uttered cries of surprise.

"No, it isn't," I shouted. I stepped into the doorway and shoved Lefty out of the way. I pushed open the screen door so Erin and April could come in. "You know Lefty's little jokes," I said, squeezing my brother against the wall.

"Lefty *is* a little joke," Erin said.

"You're stupid," Lefty told her. I pressed him into the wall a little harder, leaning against him with all my weight. But he ducked down and scooted away.

"Happy Birthday," April said, shaking the rain from her curly hair. She handed me a present, wrapped in Christmas wrapping paper. "It's the

273

only paper we had," she explained, seeing me staring at it.

"Merry Christmas to you, too," I joked. The present felt like a CD.

"I forgot your present," Erin said.

"What is it?" I asked, following the girls into the living room.

"I don't know. I haven't bought it yet."

Lefty grabbed April's present out of my hand and ran to put it on top of Zack's present in the corner behind the couch.

Erin plopped down on the white leather ottoman in front of the armchair. April stood at the window, staring out at the rain.

"We were going to barbecue hot dogs," I said.

"They'd be pretty soggy today," April replied.

Lefty stood behind the couch, tossing his softball up and catching it one-handed.

"You're going to break that lamp," I warned him.

He ignored me, of course.

"Who else is coming?" Erin asked.

Before I could answer, the doorbell rang again. Lefty and I raced to the door. He tripped over his own sneakers and went skidding down the hall on his stomach. So typical.

By two-thirty everyone had arrived, fifteen kids in all, and the party got started. Well, it didn't really get started because we couldn't decide what to do. I wanted to watch the *Terminator* movie

I'd rented. But the girls wanted to play Twister.

"It's *my* birthday!" I insisted.

We compromised. We played Twister. Then we watched some of the *Terminator* video until it was time to eat.

It was a pretty good party. I think everyone had an okay time. Even April seemed to be having fun. She was usually really quiet and nervous-looking at parties.

Lefty spilled his Coke and ate his slice of chocolate birthday cake with his hands because he thought it was funny. But he was the only animal in the group.

I told him the only reason he was invited was because he was in the family and there was nowhere else we could stash him. He replied by opening his mouth up real wide so everyone could see his chewed-up chocolate cake inside.

After I opened presents, I put the *Terminator* movie back on. But everyone started to leave. I guess it was about five o'clock. It looked much later. It was dark as night out, still storming.

My parents were in the kitchen cleaning up. Erin and April were the only ones left. Erin's mother was supposed to pick them up. She called and said she'd be a little late.

Whitey was standing at the living room window, barking his head off. I looked outside. I didn't see anyone there. I grabbed him with both hands and wrestled him away from the window.

"Let's go up to my room," I suggested when I finally got the dumb dog quiet. "I got a new Super Nintendo game I want to try."

Erin and April gladly followed me upstairs. They didn't like the *Terminator* movie, for some reason.

The upstairs hallway was pitch black. I clicked the light switch, but the overhead light didn't come on. "The bulb must be burned out," I said.

My room was at the end of the hall. We made our way slowly through the darkness.

"It's kind of spooky up here," April said quietly.

And just as she said it, the linen closet door swung open and, with a deafening howl, a dark figure leapt out at us.

2

As the girls cried out in horror, the howling creature grabbed me around the waist and wrestled me to the floor.

"Lefty — *let go!*" I screamed angrily. "You're not funny!"

He was laughing like a lunatic. He thought he was a riot. "Gotcha!" he cried. "I gotcha good!"

"We weren't scared," Erin insisted. "We knew it was you."

"Then why'd you scream?" Lefty asked.

Erin didn't have an answer.

I shoved him off me and climbed to my feet. "That was dumb, Lefty."

"How long were you waiting in the linen closet?" April asked.

"A long time," Lefty told her. He started to get up, but Whitey ran up to him and began furiously licking his face. It tickled so much, Lefty fell onto his back, laughing.

"You scared Whitey, too," I said.

"No, I didn't. Whitey's smarter than you guys."
Lefty pushed Whitey away.

Whitey began sniffing at the door across the
hall.

"Where does that door lead, Max?" Erin asked.

"To the attic," I told her.

"You have an attic?" Erin cried. Like it was
some kind of big deal. "What's up there? I *love*
attics!"

"Huh?" I squinted at her in the dark. Sometimes
girls are really weird. I mean, how could anyone
love attics?

"Just a lot of old junk my grandparents left," I
told her. "This house used to be theirs. Mom and
Dad stored a lot of their stuff in the attic. We
hardly ever go up there."

"Can we go up and take a look?" Erin asked.

"I guess," I said. "I don't think it's too big a
thrill or anything."

"I love old junk," Erin said.

"But it's so dark. . . ." April said softly. I think
she was a little scared.

I opened the door and reached for the light
switch just inside. A ceiling light clicked on in the
attic. It cast a pale yellow light down at us as we
stared up the steep wooden stairs.

"See? There's light up there," I told April. I
started up the stairs. They creaked under my
sneakers. My shadow was really long. "You coming?"

"Erin's mom will be here any minute," April said.

"We'll just go up for a second," Erin said. She gave April a gentle push. "Come on."

Whitey trotted past us as we climbed the stairs, his tail wagging excitedly, his toenails clicking loudly on the wooden steps. About halfway up, the air grew hot and dry.

I stopped on the top step and looked around. The attic stretched on both sides. It was one long room, filled with old furniture, cardboard cartons, old clothes, fishing rods, stacks of yellowed magazines — all kinds of junk.

"Ooh, it smells so musty," Erin said, moving past me and taking a few steps into the vast space. She took a deep breath. "I love that smell!"

"You're definitely weird," I told her.

Rain drummed loudly against the roof. The sound echoed through the low room, a steady roar. It sounded as if we were inside a waterfall.

All four of us began walking around, exploring. Lefty kept tossing his softball up against the ceiling rafters, then catching it as it came down. I noticed that April stayed close to Erin. Whitey was sniffing furiously along the wall.

"Think there are mice up here?" Lefty asked, a devilish grin crossing his face. I saw April's eyes go wide. "Big fat mice who like to climb up girls' legs?" Lefty teased.

My kid brother has a great sense of humor.

"Could we go now?" April asked impatiently. She started back toward the stairway.

"Look at these old magazines," Erin exclaimed, ignoring her. She picked one up and started flipping through it. "Check this out. The clothes these models are wearing are a riot!"

"Hey — what's Whitey doing?" Lefty asked suddenly.

I followed his gaze to the far wall. Behind a tall stack of cartons, I could see Whitey's tail wagging. And I could hear him scratching furiously at something.

"Whitey — come!" I commanded.

Of course he ignored me. He began scratching harder.

"Whitey, what are you scratching at?"

"Probably pulling a mouse apart," Lefty suggested.

"I'm outta here!" April exclaimed.

"Whitey?" I called. Stepping around an old dining room table, I made my way across the cluttered attic. I quickly saw that he was scratching at the bottom of a door.

"Hey, look," I called to the others. "Whitey found a hidden door."

"Cool!" Erin cried, hurrying over. Lefty and April were right behind.

"I didn't know this was up here," I said.

"We've got to check it out," Erin urged. "Let's see what's on the other side."

And that's when the trouble all began.

You can understand why I say it was all Whitey's fault, right? If that dumb dog hadn't started sniffing and scratching there, we might never have found the hidden attic room.

And we never would have discovered the exciting — and frightening — secret behind that wooden door.

3

"Whitey!" I knelt down and pulled the dog away from the door. "What's your problem, doggie?"

As soon as I moved him aside, Whitey lost all interest in the door. He trotted off and started sniffing another corner. Talk about your short attention span. But I guess that's the difference between dogs and people.

The rain continued to pound down, a steady roar just above our heads. I could hear the wind whistling around the corner of the house. It was a real spring storm.

The door had a rusted latch about halfway up. It slid off easily, and the warped wooden door started to swing open before I even pulled at it.

The door hinges squeaked as I pulled the door toward me, revealing solid darkness on the other side.

Before I had gotten the door open halfway, Lefty scooted under me and darted into the dark room.

"*A dead body!*" he shrieked.

"Noooo!" April and Erin both cried out with squeals of terror.

But I knew Lefty's dumb sense of humor. "Nice try, Lefty," I said, and followed him through the doorway.

Of course he was just goofing.

I found myself in a small, windowless room. The only light came from the pale yellow ceiling light behind us in the center of the attic.

"Push the door all the way open so the light can get in," I instructed Erin. "I can't see a thing in here."

Erin pushed open the door and slid a carton over to hold it in place. Then she and April crept in to join Lefty and me.

"It's too big to be a closet," Erin said, her voice sounding even squeakier than usual. "So what is it?"

"Just a room, I guess," I said, still waiting for my eyes to adjust to the dim light.

I took another step into the room. And as I did, a dark figure stepped toward me.

I screamed and jumped back.

The other person jumped back, too.

"It's a mirror, dork!" Lefty said, and started to laugh.

Instantly, all four of us were laughing. Nervous, high-pitched laughter.

It *was* a mirror in front of us. In the pale yellow

light filtering into the small, square room, I could see it clearly now.

It was a big, rectangular mirror, about two feet taller than me, with a dark wood frame. It rested on a wooden base.

I moved closer to it and my reflection moved once again to greet me. To my surprise, the reflection was clear. No dust on the glass, despite the fact that no one had been in here in ages.

I stepped in front of it and started to check out my hair.

I mean, that's what mirrors are for, right?

"Who would put a mirror in a room all by itself?" Erin asked. I could see her dark reflection in the mirror, a few feet behind me.

"Maybe it's a valuable piece of furniture or something," I said, reaching into my jeans pocket for my comb. "You know. An antique."

"Did your parents put it up here?" Erin asked.

"I don't know," I replied. "Maybe it belonged to my grandparents. I just don't know." I ran the comb through my hair a few times.

"Can we go now? This isn't too thrilling," April said. She was still lingering reluctantly in the doorway.

"Maybe it was a carnival mirror," Lefty said, pushing me out of the way and making faces into the mirror, bringing his face just inches from the glass. "You know. One of those fun house mirrors that makes your body look like it's shaped like an egg."

"You're already shaped like an egg," I joked, pushing him aside. "At least, your head is."

"You're a *rotten* egg," he snapped back. "You stink."

I peered into the mirror. I looked perfectly normal, not distorted at all. "Hey, April, come in," I urged. "You're blocking most of the light."

"Can't we just leave?" she asked, whining. Reluctantly, she moved from the doorway, taking a few small steps into the room. "Who cares about an old mirror, anyway?"

"Hey, look," I said, pointing. I had spotted a light attached to the top of the mirror. It was oval-shaped, made of brass or some other kind of metal. The bulb was long and narrow, almost like a fluorescent bulb, only shorter.

I gazed up at it, trying to figure it out in the dim light. "How do you turn it on, I wonder."

"There's a chain," Erin said, coming up beside me.

Sure enough, a slender chain descended from the right side of the lamp, hanging down about a foot from the top of the mirror.

"Wonder if it works," I said.

"The bulb's probably dead," Lefty remarked. Good old Lefty. Always an optimist.

"Only one way to find out," I said. Standing on

tiptoes, I stretched my hand up to the chain.

"Be careful," April warned.

"Huh? It's just a light," I told her.

Famous last words.

I reached up. Missed. Tried again. I grabbed the chain on the second try and pulled.

The light came on with a startlingly bright flash. Then it dimmed down to normal light. Very white light that reflected brightly in the mirror.

"Hey — that's better!" I exclaimed. "It lights up the whole room. Pretty bright, huh?"

No one said anything.

"I *said*, pretty bright, huh?"

Still silence from my companions.

I turned around and was surprised to find looks of horror on all three faces.

"Max?" Lefty cried, staring hard at me, his eyes practically popping out of his head.

"Max — where are you?" Erin cried. She turned to April."Where'd he go?"

"I'm right here," I told them. "I haven't moved."

"But we can't see you!" April cried.

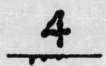

4

All three of them were staring in my direction with their eyes bulging and looks of horror still on their faces. But I could tell they were goofing.

"Give me a break, guys," I said. "I'm not as stupid as I look. No way I'm falling for your dumb joke."

"But, Max — " Lefty insisted. "We're *serious!*"

"We can't see you!" Erin repeated.

Dumb, dumb, dumb.

Suddenly, the light started to hurt my eyes. It seemed to grow brighter. It was shining right in my face.

Shielding my eyes with one hand, I reached up with the other hand and pulled the chain.

The light went out, but the white glare stayed with me. I tried to blink it away, but I still saw large bright spots before my eyes.

"Hey — you're back!" Lefty cried. He stepped up and grabbed my arm and squeezed it, as if he were testing it, making sure I was real or something.

"What's your problem?" I snapped. I was starting to get angry. "I didn't fall for your dumb joke, Lefty. So why keep it up?"

To my surprise, Lefty didn't back away. He held onto my arm as if he were afraid to let go.

"We weren't joking, Max," Erin insisted in a low voice. "We really couldn't see you."

"It must have been the light in the mirror," April said. She was pressed against the wall next to the doorway. "It was so bright. I think it was just an optical illusion or something."

"It *wasn't* an optical illusion," Erin told her. "I was standing right next to Max. And I couldn't see him."

"He was invisible," Lefty added solemnly.

I laughed. "You guys are trying to scare me," I said. "And you're doing a pretty good job of it!"

"You scared *us!*" Lefty exclaimed. He let go of my arm and stepped up to the mirror.

I followed his gaze. "There I am," I said, pointing to my reflection. A strand of hair was poking up in back of my head. I carefully slicked it down.

"Let's get out of here," April pleaded.

Lefty started to toss his softball up, studying himself in the mirror.

Erin made her way around to the back of the mirror. "It's too dark back here. I can't see anything," she said.

She stepped around to the front and stared up at the oval-shaped lamp on top. "You disappeared as soon as you pulled the chain on that lamp."

"You're really serious!" I said. For the first time I began to believe they weren't joking.

"You were invisible, Max," Erin said. "Poof. You were gone."

"She's right," Lefty agreed, tossing the softball up and catching it, admiring his form in the mirror.

"It was just an optical illusion," April insisted. "Why are you guys making such a big deal about it?"

"It *wasn't*!" Erin insisted.

"He clicked on the light. Then he disappeared in a flash," Lefty said. He dropped the softball. It bounced loudly on the hardwood floor, then rolled behind the mirror.

He hesitated for a few seconds. Then he went after it, diving for the ball in the darkness. A few seconds later, he came running back.

"You really were invisible, Max," he said.

"Really," Erin added, staring hard at me.

"Prove it," I told them.

"Let's *go*!" April pleaded. She had moved to the doorway and was standing half in, half out of the room.

"What do you mean *prove it*?" Erin asked, talking to my dark reflection in the mirror.

"Show me," I said.

"You mean do what you did?" Erin asked, turning to talk to the real me.

"Yeah," I said. "You go invisible, too. Just like I did."

Erin and Lefty stared at me. Lefty's mouth dropped open.

"This is dumb," April called from behind us.

"I'll do it," Lefty said. He stepped up to the mirror.

I pulled him back by the shoulders. "Not you," I said. "You're too young."

He tried to pull out of my grasp, but I held onto him. "How about you, Erin?" I urged, wrapping my arms around Lefty's waist to keep him back from the mirror.

She shrugged. "Okay. I'll try, I guess."

Lefty stopped struggling to get away. I loosened my grip a little.

We watched Erin step up in front of the mirror. Her reflection stared back at her, dark and shadowy.

She stood on tiptoes, reached up, and grabbed the lamp chain. She glanced over at me and smiled. "Here goes," she said.

5

The chain slipped from Erin's hand.

She reached up and grabbed it again.

She was just about to tug at it when a woman's voice interrupted from downstairs. "Erin! Are you up there? April?"

I recognized the voice. Erin's mom.

"Yeah. We're up here," Erin shouted. She let go of the chain.

"Hurry down. We're late!" her mom called. "What are you doing up in the attic, anyway?"

"Nothing," Erin called down. She turned to me and shrugged.

"Good. I'm *outta* here!" April exclaimed, and hurried to the stairway.

We all followed her down, clumping noisily down the creaking wooden stairs.

"What were you doing up there?" my mom asked when we were all in the living room. "It's so dusty in that attic. It's a wonder you're not filthy."

291

"We were just hanging out," I told her.

"We were playing with an old mirror," Lefty said. "It was kind of neat."

"Playing with a mirror?" Erin's mom flashed my mom a bewildered glance.

"See you guys," Erin said, pulling her mom to the door. "Great party, Max."

"Yeah. Thanks," April added.

They headed out the front door. The rain had finally stopped. I stood at the screen door and watched them step around the puddles on the walk as they made their way to the car.

When I turned back into the living room, Lefty was tossing the softball up to the ceiling, trying to catch it behind his back. He missed. The ball bounced up from the floor onto an end table, where it knocked over a large vase of tulips.

What a crash!

The vase shattered. Tulips went flying. All the water poured down onto the carpet.

Mom tossed up her hands and said something silently up to the sky, the way she always does when she's very pushed out of shape about something.

Then she really got on Lefty's case. She started screaming: "How many times do I have to tell you not to throw that ball in the house?" Stuff like that. She kept it up for quite a while.

Lefty shrank into a corner and tried to make himself tinier and tinier. He kept saying he was sorry, but Mom was yelling so loud, I don't think she heard him.

I bet Lefty wanted to be invisible right at that moment.

But he had to stand and take his punishment. Then he and I helped clean up the mess.

A few minutes later, I saw him tossing the softball up in the living room again.

That's the thing about Lefty. He never learns.

I didn't think about the mirror again for a couple of days. I got busy with school and other stuff. Rehearsing for the spring concert. I'm only in the chorus, but I still have to go to every rehearsal.

I saw Erin and April in school a lot. But neither of them mentioned the mirror. I guess maybe it slipped their minds, too. Or maybe we all just shut it out of our minds.

It was kind of scary, if you stopped to think about it.

I mean, *if* you believed what they said happened.

Then that Wednesday night I couldn't get to sleep. I was lying there, staring up at the ceiling, watching the shadows sway back and forth.

I tried counting sheep. I tried shutting my eyes real tight and counting backwards from one thousand.

But I was really keyed up, for some reason. Not at all sleepy.

Suddenly I found myself thinking about the mirror up in the attic.

What was it doing up there? I asked myself. Why was it closed up in that hidden room with the door carefully latched?

Who did it belong to? My grandparents? If so, why would they hide it in that tiny room?

I wondered if Mom and Dad even knew it was up there.

I started thinking about what had happened on Saturday after my birthday party. I pictured myself standing in front of the mirror. Combing my hair. Then reaching for the chain. Pulling it. The flash of bright light as the lamp went on. And then . . .

Did I see my reflection in the mirror after the light went on?

I couldn't remember.

Did I see myself at all? My hands? My feet?

I couldn't remember.

"It was a joke," I said aloud, lying in my bed, kicking the covers off me.

It had to be a joke.

Lefty was always playing dumb jokes on me, trying to make me look bad. My brother was a joker. He'd always been a joker. He was never serious. Never.

So what made me think he was serious now?

Because Erin and April had agreed with him?

Before I realized it, I had climbed out of bed.

Only one way to find out if they were serious or not, I told myself. I searched in the darkness for my bedroom slippers. I buttoned my pajama shirt which had come undone from all my tossing and turning.

Then, as silent as I could be, I crept out into the hallway.

The house was dark except for the tiny night-light down by the floor just outside Lefty's bedroom. Lefty was the only one in the family who ever got up in the middle of the night. He insisted on having a night-light in his room and one in the hall, even though I made fun of him about it as often as I could.

Now I was grateful for the light as I made my way on tiptoe to the attic stairs. Even though I was being so careful, the floorboards squeaked under my feet. It's just impossible not to make noise in an old house like this.

I stopped and held my breath, listening hard, listening for any sign that I had been heard.

Silence.

Taking a deep breath, I opened the attic door, fumbled around till I found the light switch, and clicked on the attic light. Then I made my way slowly up the steep stairs, leaning all my weight on the banister, trying my hardest not to make the stairs creak.

It seemed to take forever to get all the way up. Finally, I stopped at the top step and gazed around, letting my eyes adjust to the yellow glare of the ceiling light.

The attic was hot and stuffy. The air was so dry, it made my nose burn. I had a sudden urge to turn around and go back.

But then my eyes stopped at the doorway to the small, hidden room. In our hurry to leave, we had left the door wide open.

Staring at the darkness beyond the open doorway, I stepped onto the landing and made my way quickly across the cluttered floor. The floorboards creaked and groaned beneath me, but I barely heard them.

I was drawn to the open doorway, drawn to the mysterious room as if being pulled by a powerful magnet.

I had to see the tall mirror again. I had to examine it, study it closely.

I had to know the truth about it.

I stepped into the small room without hesitating and walked up to the mirror.

I paused for a moment and studied my shadowy reflection in the glass. My hair was totally messed up, but I didn't care.

I stared at myself, stared into my eyes. Then I took a step back to get a different view.

The mirror reflected my entire body from head to foot. There wasn't anything special about the reflection. It wasn't distorted or weird in any way.

The fact that it was such a normal reflection

296

helped to calm me. I hadn't realized it, but my heart was fluttering like a nervous butterfly. My hands and feet were cold as ice.

"Chill out, Max," I whispered to myself, watching myself whisper in the dark mirror.

I did a funny little dance for my own benefit, waving my hands above my head and shaking my whole body.

"Nothing special about this mirror," I said aloud.

I reached out and touched it. The glass felt cool despite the warmth of the room. I ran my hand along the glass until I reached the frame. Then I let my hand wander up and down the wood frame. It also felt smooth and cool.

It's just a mirror, I thought, finally feeling more relaxed. Just an old mirror that someone stored up here long ago and forgot about.

Still holding onto the frame, I walked around to the back. It was too dark to see clearly, but it didn't seem too interesting back here.

Well, I might as well turn on the light at the top, I thought.

I returned to the front of the mirror. Standing just inches back from it, I began to reach up for the lamp chain when something caught my eye.

"Oh!"

I cried out as I saw two eyes, down low in the mirror. Two eyes staring out at me.

6

My breath caught in my throat. I peered down into the dark reflection.

The two eyes peered up at me. Dark and evil eyes.

Uttering a cry of panic, I turned away from the mirror.

"Lefty!" I cried. My voice came out shrill and tight, as if someone were squeezing my throat.

He grinned at me from just inside the doorway.

I realized that it had been Lefty's eyes reflected in the mirror.

I ran over to him and grabbed him by the shoulders. "You scared me to death!" I half-screamed, half-whispered.

His grin grew wider. "You're stupid," he said.

I wanted to strangle him. He thought it was a riot.

"Why'd you sneak up behind me?" I demanded, giving him a shove back against the wall.

He shrugged.

"Well, what are you doing up here, anyway?" I sputtered.

I could still see those dark eyes staring out at me in the mirror. So creepy!

"I heard you," he explained, leaning back against the wall, still grinning. "I was awake. I heard you walk past my room. So I followed you."

"Well, you shouldn't be up here," I snapped.

"Neither should you," he snapped back.

"Go back downstairs and go to bed," I said. My voice was finally returning to normal. I tried to sound as if I meant business.

But Lefty didn't move. "Make me," he said. Another classic argument-winner.

"I mean it," I insisted. "Go back to bed."

"Make me," he repeated nastily. "I'll tell Mom and Dad you're up here," he added.

I hate being threatened. And he knows it. That's why he threatens me every hour of the day.

Sometimes I just wish I could pound him.

But we live in a nonviolent family.

That's what Mom and Dad say every time Lefty and I get in a fight. "Break it up, you two. We live in a nonviolent family."

Sometimes nonviolence can be real frustrating. Know what I mean?

This was one of those times. But I could see that I wasn't going to get rid of Lefty so easily. He was determined to stay up in the attic with me and see what I was doing with the mirror.

My heart had finally slowed down to normal. I was starting to feel calmer. So I decided to stop fighting with him and let him stay. I turned back to the mirror.

Luckily, there wasn't *another* pair of eyes in there staring out at me!

"What are you doing?" Lefty demanded, stepping up behind me, his arms still crossed over his chest.

"Just checking out the mirror," I told him.

"You going to go invisible again?" he asked. He was standing right behind me, and his breath smelled sour, like lemons.

I turned and shoved him back a few steps. "Get out of my face," I said. "Your breath stinks."

That started another stupid argument, of course.

I was sorry I'd ever come up here. I should have stayed in bed, I realized.

Finally, I persuaded him to stand a foot away from me. A major victory.

Yawning, I turned back to the mirror. I was starting to feel sleepy. Maybe it was because of the heat of the attic. Maybe it was because I was tired of arguing with my dopey brother. Or maybe it was because it was really late at night, and I was tired.

"I'm going to turn on the light," I told him, reaching for the chain. "Tell me if I go invisible again."

"No." He shoved his way right next to me again. "I want to try it, too."

"No way," I insisted, shoving back.

"Yes *way*." He pushed me hard.

I pushed back. Then I had a better idea. "How about if we *both* stand in front of the mirror, and I pull the light chain?"

"Okay. Go ahead." Standing an inch in front of it, practically nose to nose with his reflection, Lefty stiffened until he was standing at attention.

He looked ridiculous, especially in those awful green pajamas.

I stepped up beside him. "Here goes nothing," I said.

I stretched my hand up, grabbed the light chain, and pulled.

7

The light on top of the mirror flashed.

"Ow!" I cried out. The light was so bright, it hurt my eyes.

Then it quickly dimmed, and my eyes started to adjust.

I turned to Lefty and started to say something. I don't remember what it was. It completely flew out of my mind when I realized that Lefty was gone.

"L-Lefty?" I stammered.

"I'm right here," he replied. His voice sounded nearby, but I couldn't see him. "Max — where are *you*?"

"You can't see me?" I cried.

"No," Lefty said. "No, I can't."

I could smell his sour breath, so I knew he was there. But he was invisible. Gone. Out of sight.

So they *weren't* putting me on! Erin, April, and Lefty had been telling the truth on Saturday after my birthday party. I really had gone invisible.

And now I was invisible again, along with my brother.

"Hey, Max," his voice sounded tiny, shaky. "This is weird."

"Yeah. It's weird, okay," I agreed. "You really can't see me, Lefty?"

"No. And I can't see myself," he said.

The mirror. I had forgotten to check out the mirror.

Did I have a reflection?

I turned and stared into the mirror. The light was pouring down from the top of the frame, casting a bright glare over the glass.

Squinting into the glare, I saw . . . *nothing*.

No me.

No Lefty.

Just the reflection of the wall behind us and the open doorway leading to the rest of the attic.

"We — we don't have reflections," I said.

"It's kinda cool," Lefty remarked. He grabbed my arm. I jumped in surprise.

"Hey!" I cried.

It felt creepy to be grabbed by an invisible person.

I grabbed him back. I tickled his ribs. He started to laugh.

"We still have our bodies," I said. "We just can't see them."

He tried to tickle me, but I danced away from him.

303

"Hey, Max, where'd you go?" he called, sounding frightened again.

"Try and find me," I teased, backing toward the wall.

"I — I can't," he said shakily. "Come back over here, okay?"

"No way," I said. "I don't want to be tickled."

"I won't," Lefty swore. "I promise."

I stepped back in front of the mirror.

"Are you here?" Lefty asked timidly.

"Yeah. I'm right beside you. I can smell your bad breath," I told him.

And he started to tickle me again. The little liar.

We wrestled around for a bit. It was just so strange wrestling with someone you couldn't see.

Finally, I pushed him away. "I wonder if we could go downstairs and still be invisible," I said. "I wonder if we could leave the house like this."

"And go spy on people?" Lefty suggested.

"Yeah," I said. I yawned. I was starting to feel a little strange. "We could go spy on girls and stuff."

"Cool," Lefty replied.

"Remember that old movie Mom and Dad were watching on TV?" I asked him. "About the ghosts who kept appearing and disappearing all the time? They had a lot of fun scaring people. You know, playing jokes on them, driving them crazy."

"But we're not ghosts," Lefty replied in a trem-

304

bling voice. I think the idea kind of frightened him.

It frightened me, too!

"Could we go back to normal now?" Lefty asked. "I don't feel right."

"Me, either," I told him. I was feeling very light. Kind of fluttery. Just . . . weird.

"How can we get back right again?" he asked.

"Well, the last time, I just pulled the chain. I clicked the light off, and I was back. That's all it took."

"Well, do it," Lefty urged impatiently. "Right now. Okay?"

"Yeah. Okay." I started to feel kind of dizzy. Kind of light. As if I could float away or something.

"Hurry," Lefty said. I could hear him breathing hard.

I reached up and grabbed the light chain. "No problem," I told him. "We'll be back in a second."

I pulled the chain.

The light went out.

But Lefty and I didn't return.

8

"Max — I can't see you!" Lefty whined.

"I know," I replied quietly. I felt so frightened. I had chills running down my back, chills that wouldn't stop. "I can't see you, either."

"What happened?" Lefty cried. I could feel him tug at my invisible arm.

"I — I don't know," I stammered. "It worked before. I clicked off the light and I was back."

I gazed into the mirror. No reflection. Nothing. No me. No Lefty.

I stood there, staring at the spot where our reflections should be, frozen with fear. I was glad Lefty couldn't see me because I wouldn't want him to see how frightened I looked.

"Try it again, Max," he whined. "Please. Hurry!"

"Okay," I said. "Just try to stay calm, okay?"

"Stay calm? How?" Lefty wailed. "What if we *never* get back? What if *no one* can ever see us again?"

I suddenly felt so sick. My stomach just sort of heaved.

Get a grip, I told myself. You've *got* to keep it together, Max. For Lefty's sake.

I stretched up for the light chain, but it seemed to be out of my reach.

I tried again. Missed.

And then suddenly, I was back. And so was Lefty.

We could see each other. And we could see our reflections in the mirror.

"We're *back!*" We both shouted it in unison.

And then we both fell on the floor, laughing. We were so relieved. So happy.

"Ssshh!" I grabbed Lefty and shoved my hand over his mouth. I just remembered it was the middle of the night. "If Mom and Dad catch us up here, they'll kill us," I warned, whispering.

"Why did it take so long for us to come back?" Lefty asked, turning serious, gazing at his reflection.

I shrugged. "Beats me." I thought about it. "Maybe if you stay invisible longer, it takes longer for you to get back," I suggested.

"Huh? What do you mean?"

"The first time I went invisible," I told him, "it was only for a few seconds. And I came back instantly, as soon as I clicked off the light. But tonight — "

"We stayed invisible a lot longer. So it took

307

longer to come back. I get it," Lefty said.

"You're not as dumb as you look," I said, yawning.

"*You* are!" he snapped back.

Feeling totally exhausted, I started to lead the way out of the tiny room, motioning for Lefty to follow me. But he hesitated, glancing back at his reflection in the mirror.

"We have to tell Mom and Dad about the mirror," he whispered thoughtfully.

"No way!" I told him. "No way we're telling them. If we tell them about it, they'll take it away. They won't let us use it."

He stared at me thoughtfully. "I'm not sure I *want* to use it," he said softly.

"Well, I do," I said, turning at the doorway to look back at it. "I want to use it just one more time."

"What for?" Lefty asked, yawning.

"To scare Zack," I said, grinning.

Zack couldn't come over until Saturday. As soon as he arrived, I wanted to take him up to the attic and give him a demonstration of the mirror's powers.

Mainly, I wanted to scare the life out of him!

But Mom insisted that we sit down for lunch first. Canned chicken noodle soup and peanut butter-and-jelly sandwiches.

I gulped my soup as fast as I could, not bothering to chew the noodles. Lefty kept giving me meaningful glances across the table. I could see that he was as eager as I was to scare Zack.

"Where'd you get that haircut?" my mom asked Zack. She walked around the table, staring at Zack's head, frowning. I could tell she *hated* it.

"At Quick Cuts," Zack told her after swallowing a mouthful of peanut butter and jelly. "You know. At the mall."

We all studied Zack's haircut. I thought it was kind of cool. The way it was buzzed so short on the left, then hung down long on the right.

"It's different, all right," my mom said.

We all could tell she hated it. But I guess she thought she was covering up by calling it *different*. If I ever came home with a haircut like that, she'd *murder* me!

"What did your mom say about it?" she asked Zack.

Zack laughed. "Not much."

We all laughed. I kept glancing up at the clock. I was so eager to get upstairs.

"How about some chocolate cupcakes?" Mom asked when we'd finished our sandwiches.

Zack started to say yes, but I interrupted him. "Can we have dessert later? I'm kinda full."

I pushed back my chair and got up quickly, motioning for Zack to follow me. Lefty was already running to the stairs.

"Hey — where are you going so fast?" Mom called after us, following us into the hall.

"Uh . . . upstairs . . . to the attic," I told her.

"The attic?" She wrinkled her face, puzzled. "What's so interesting up there?"

"Uh . . . just a bunch of old magazines," I lied. "They're kind of funny. I want to show them to Zack." That was pretty fast thinking, for me. I'm usually not very quick at making up stories.

Mom stared at me. I don't think she believed me. But she turned back to the kitchen. "Have fun, guys. Don't get too dirty up there."

"We won't," I told her. I led Zack up the steep stairs. Lefty was already waiting for us in the attic.

It was about a hundred degrees hotter up there. I started to sweat the second I stepped into the room.

Zack stopped a few feet behind me and looked around. "It's just a lot of old junk. What's so interesting up here?" he asked.

"You'll see," I said mysteriously.

"This way," Lefty called eagerly, running to the little room against the far wall. He was so excited, he dropped his softball. It rolled in front of him, and he tripped over it and fell facedown on the floor with a *thud*.

"I *meant* to do that!" Lefty joked, climbing up quickly and leaping after the ball, which had rolled across the floor.

"Your brother is made of rubber or something," Zack laughed.

"Falling down is his hobby," I said. "He falls down about a hundred times a day." I wasn't exaggerating.

A few seconds later, the three of us were in the hidden room standing in front of the mirror. Even though it was a sunny afternoon, the room was as dark and shadowy as ever.

Zack turned from the mirror to me, a bewildered look on his face. "*This* is what you wanted to show me?"

"Yeah." I nodded.

"Since when are you into furniture?" he asked.

"It's an interesting mirror, don't you think?" I asked.

"No," he said. "Not too interesting."

Lefty laughed. He bounced his softball off the wall and caught it.

I was deliberately taking my time. Zack was in for the surprise of his life, but I wanted to confuse him a little bit first. He was always doing stuff like that to me. He always acted as if he knew everything there was to know, and if I were good, he'd share a little bit of his knowledge with me.

Well, now I knew something he didn't know. I wanted to stretch this moment out, make it last.

But at the same time, I couldn't wait to watch the look on Zack's face when I disappeared right in front of his eyes.

"Let's go outside," Zack said impatiently. "It's too hot up here. I brought my bike. Why don't we ride to the playground behind school, see who's there?"

"Maybe later," I replied, grinning at Lefty. I turned to my brother. "Should I show Zack our secret or not?"

Lefty grinned back at me. He shrugged.

"What secret?" Zack demanded. I knew he couldn't stand to be left out of anything. He couldn't *bear* it if anyone had a secret he didn't know about.

"What secret?" he repeated when I didn't answer.

"Show him," Lefty said, tossing up the softball.

I rubbed my chin, pretended to be thinking about it. "Well . . . okay." I motioned for Zack to stand behind me.

"You're going to make funny faces in the mirror?" Zack guessed. He shook his head. "Big deal!"

"No. That's not the secret," I told him. I stepped in front of the mirror, admiring my reflection, which stared back at me in the glass.

"Watch!" Lefty urged, stepping up beside Zack.

"I'm watching. I'm watching," Zack said impatiently.

"I'll bet you I can disappear into thin air," I told Zack.

"Yeah. Sure," he muttered.

Lefty laughed.

"How much do you want to bet?" I asked.

"Two cents," Zack said. "Is this some kind of trick mirror or something?"

"Something like that," I told him. "How about ten dollars? Bet me ten dollars?"

"Huh?"

"Forget the bet. Just show him," Lefty said, bouncing up and down impatiently.

"I have a magic kit at home," Zack said. "I can do over a thousand tricks. But it's kid stuff," he sneered.

"You don't have any tricks like this," I said confidently.

"Just get it over with so we can go outside," he grumbled.

I stepped into the center of the mirror. "Ta-daa!" I sang myself a short fanfare. Then I reached up and grabbed the light chain.

I pulled it. The lamp above the mirror flashed on, blindingly bright at first, then dimming as before.

And I was gone.

"Hey!" Zack cried. He stumbled backwards.

He actually stumbled out of shock!

Invisible, I turned away from the mirror to enjoy his stunned reaction.

"Max?" he cried out. His eyes searched the room.

Lefty was laughing his head off.

"Max?" Zack sounded really worried. "Max? How'd you do that? Where *are* you?"

"I'm right here," I said.

He jumped at the sound of my voice. Lefty laughed even harder.

I reached out and took the softball from Lefty's hand. I glanced at the reflection in the mirror. The ball seemed to float in midair.

"Here. Catch, Zack." I tossed it at him.

He was so stunned, he didn't move. The ball bounced off his chest. "Max? How do you do this trick?" he demanded.

"It isn't a trick. It's real," I said.

"Hey, wait . . ." He got a suspicious look on his face. He ran around to the back of the mirror. I guess he expected me to be hiding back there.

He looked very disappointed when he didn't see me. "Is there a trapdoor or something?" he asked. He walked back in front of the mirror, got down on his hands and knees, and started searching the floorboards for a trapdoor.

I leaned over and pulled his T-shirt up over his head.

"Hey — stop it!" he yelled, climbing angrily to his feet.

I tickled his stomach.

"Stop, Max." He squirmed away, thrashing his arms, trying to hit me. He looked really frightened now. He was breathing hard, and his face was bright red.

I pulled his T-shirt up again.

He jerked it down. "You're really invisible?" His voice rose up so high, only dogs could hear it. "Really?"

"Good trick, huh?" I said right in his ear.

He jumped and spun away. "What does it feel like? Does it feel weird?"

I didn't answer him. I crept out of the room and picked up a cardboard carton just outside the door. I carried it up to the mirror. It looked great. A carton floating all by itself.

"Put it down," Zack urged. He sounded really scared. "This is really freaking me out, Max. Stop it, okay? Come back so I can see you."

I wanted to torture him some more, but I could see he was about to lose it. Besides, I was starting to feel weird again. Sort of dizzy and lightheaded. And the bright light was hurting my eyes, starting to blind me.

"Okay, I'm coming back," I announced. "Watch."

I leaned against the mirror and reached up for the chain. I suddenly felt very tired, very weak. It took all my strength to wrap my hand around the chain.

I had the strangest sensation that the mirror was pulling me, tugging me toward it, holding me down.

With a determined burst of strength, I pulled the chain.

The lamp went out. The room darkened.

"Where are you? I still can't see you!" Zack cried, his voice revealing panic.

"Just chill," I told him. "It takes a few seconds. The longer I stay invisible, the longer it takes to come back." And then I added, "I think."

Staring into the blank mirror, waiting for my reflection to return, I suddenly realized that I didn't know anything at all about this mirror, about turning invisible. About coming back.

My mind suddenly whirred with all sorts of terrifying questions:

What made me think that reappearing was automatic?

What if you could only come back twice? And after the third time you went invisible, you stayed invisible?

What if the mirror was broken? What if it was locked away in this hidden room because it didn't work properly and it made people stay invisible forever?

What if I never came back?

No, that can't be, I told myself.

But the seconds were ticking by. And my body was still not visible.

I touched the mirror, rubbing my invisible hand over the smooth, cool glass.

"Max, what's taking so long?" Zack asked, his voice trembling.

"I don't know," I told him, sounding as frightened and upset as he did.

And then suddenly, I was back.

I was staring at my reflection in the mirror, watching intently, gratefully, as a wide smile crossed my face.

"Ta-*daaa!*" I sang my triumphant fanfare, turning to my still shaken friend. "Here I am!"

"Wow!" Zack exclaimed, and his mouth remained in a tight O of surprise and wonder. "Wow."

"I know," I said, grinning. "Pretty cool, huh?"

I felt very shaky, kind of trembly all over. My knees felt all weak and sweaty. You know the feeling.

But I ignored it. I wanted to enjoy my moment of glory. It wasn't often that I got to do something that Zack hadn't already done ten times.

"Amazing," Zack said, staring hard at the mirror. "I've *got* to try it!"

"Well . . ." I wasn't so sure I wanted Zack to do it. It was such a big responsibility. I mean, what if something went wrong?

"You've *got* to let me do it!" Zack insisted.

"Hey — where's Lefty?" I asked, glancing quickly around the small room.

"Huh? Lefty?" Zack's eyes searched, too.

"I was so busy being invisible, I forgot he was here," I said. And then I called, "Hey, Lefty?"

No reply.

"Lefty?"

Silence.

I walked quickly around to the back of the mirror. He wasn't there. Calling his name, I made my way to the door and peered out into the attic.

No sign of him.

"He was standing right here. In front of the mirror," Zack said, suddenly pale.

"Lefty?" I called. "Are you here? Can you hear me?"

Silence.

"Weird," Zack said.

I swallowed hard. My stomach suddenly felt as if I'd swallowed a rock.

"He was right here. Standing right here," Zack said in a shrill, frightened voice.

"Well, he's gone now," I said, staring at the dark, shadowy reflection of the mirror. "Lefty's gone."

9

"Maybe Lefty went invisible, too," Zack suggested.

"Then why doesn't he answer us?" I cried. I tried calling my brother again. "Lefty — are you here? Can you hear me?"

No reply.

I walked up to the mirror and angrily slapped the frame. "Stupid mirror."

"Lefty? Lefty?" Zack had his hands cupped around his mouth like a megaphone. He stood at the door to the little room, calling out into the attic.

"I don't believe this," I said weakly. My legs were shaking so much, I dropped down onto the floor.

And then I heard giggling.

"Huh? Lefty?" I jumped to my feet.

More giggling. Coming from behind the carton I'd carried into the little room.

I lunged toward the carton just as Lefty popped

up from behind it. "Gotcha!" he cried, and collapsed over the carton, slapping the floor, laughing his head off.

"Gotcha! Gotcha both!"

"You little creep!" Zack screamed.

He and I both pounced on Lefty at the same time. I pulled his arm back until he screamed. Zack messed up his hair, then tickled him.

Lefty was screaming and laughing and squirming and crying all at the same time. I gave him a hard punch on the shoulder. "Don't ever do that again," I shouted angrily.

Lefty laughed, so I gave him a hard shove and climbed to my feet.

Zack and I, both breathing hard, both red in the face, glared angrily at Lefty. He was rolling around on the floor, covered in dust, still laughing like a lunatic.

"You scared us to death. You really did!" I exclaimed heatedly.

"I know," Lefty replied happily.

"Let's beat him up some more," Zack suggested, balling his hands into tight fists.

"Okay," I agreed.

"You'll have to catch me first!" Lefty cried. He was on his feet in a flash, and out the door.

I chased after him, tripped over a stack of old clothes, and went flying headfirst to the floor. "Ow!" I banged my leg hard. The pain shot up through my body.

Pulling myself up slowly, I started after Lefty again. But voices on the attic stairway made me stop.

Erin's head popped up first. Then April appeared.

Lefty was sitting on the windowsill at the far end of the attic, red-faced and sweaty, catching his breath.

"Hey, how's it going?" I called to the two girls, brushing dust off my jeans, then straightening my hair with one hand.

"Your mom said you were here," Erin explained, looking from Lefty to me.

"What are you guys *doing* up here?" April asked.

"Oh . . . just hanging out," I said, casting an angry glance at my brother, who stuck his tongue out in reply.

April picked up an old *Life* magazine from a stack of yellowed magazines and began flipping through it. But the pages crumbled as she looked at them. "Yuck," she said, putting it down. "This stuff is so old."

"That's what attics are for," I said, starting to feel a little more normal. "Whoever heard of keeping *new* stuff in an attic?"

"Ha-ha," Lefty laughed sarcastically.

"Where's that mirror?" Erin asked, stepping into the center of the room. "The one that made that weird optical illusion last Saturday."

"It wasn't an optical illusion," I blurted out. I didn't really feel like messing with the mirror anymore. I'd had enough scares for one afternoon. But the words just tumbled out of me.

I can never keep a secret. It's a real character flaw.

"What do you mean?" Erin asked, very interested. She walked past me, heading to the open doorway of the little room.

"You mean that wasn't an optical illusion last week?" April asked, following her.

"No, not really," I said, glancing at Lefty, who hadn't budged from the windowsill across the large room. "The mirror has strange powers or something. It really can turn you invisible."

April laughed scornfully. "Yeah. Right," she said. "And I'm going to fly to Mars in a flying saucer tonight after dinner."

"Give me a break," I muttered. I turned my eyes to Erin. "I'm serious."

Erin stared back at me, her face filled with doubt. "You're trying to tell us that you've gone in that room and become invisible?"

"I'm not *trying* to tell you," I replied heatedly. "I *am* telling you!"

April laughed.

Erin continued to stare at me, studying my face. "You *are* serious," she decided.

"It's a trick mirror," April told her. "That's all.

322

That light on top of it is so bright, it makes your eyes go weird."

"Show us," Erin said to me.

"Yeah. Show them!" Lefty exclaimed eagerly. He jumped up from the windowsill and started running to the little room. "I'll go this time! Let me do it!"

"No way," I said.

"Let *me* try it," Erin volunteered.

"Hey, do you know who else is here?" I asked the girls, following them to the room. "Zack is here." I called to him. "Hey, Zack. Erin wants to go invisible. Think we should let her?"

I stepped into the room. "Zack?"

"Where's he hiding?" Erin asked.

I uttered a silent gasp.

The mirror light was on. Zack was gone.

10

"Oh, no!" I cried. "I don't believe this!"

Lefty laughed. "Zack's invisible," he told Erin and April.

"Zack — where are you?" I demanded angrily.

Suddenly, the softball floated up from Lefty's hand. "Hey, give that back!" Lefty shouted, and grabbed for it. But invisible Zack pulled the ball out of Lefty's reach.

Erin and April were both gaping at the ball as it floated in midair, their eyes bulging, their mouths wide open.

"Hi, girls," Zack called in a booming, deep voice that floated from in front of the mirror.

April screamed and grabbed Erin's arm.

"Zack, stop kidding around. How long have you been invisible?" I asked.

"I don't know." The ball flew back to Lefty, who dropped it and had to chase it out into the attic.

"How long, Zack?" I repeated.

"About five minutes, maybe," he replied.

"When you chased after Lefty, I turned on the light and went invisible. Then I heard you talking to Erin and April."

"You've been invisible the whole time?" I asked, feeling really nervous and upset.

"Yeah. This is awesome!" he exclaimed. But then his tone grew doubtful. "I — I'm starting to feel kinda funny, though, Max."

"Funny?" Erin asked, staring at where Zack's voice seemed to be coming from. "What do you mean 'funny'?"

"Kinda dizzy," Zack replied weakly. "Everything's kind of breaking up. You know. Like a bad TV picture. I mean, you're starting to fade, to seem far away."

"I'm bringing you back," I said. And without waiting for Zack to reply, I reached up and pulled the light chain.

The light clicked off. Darkness seemed to roll into the room, filling the mirror with gray shadows.

"Where *is* he?" April cried. "It didn't work. He isn't back."

"It takes a while," I explained.

"How long?" April asked.

"I don't really know," I said.

"Why aren't I back?" Zack asked. He was standing right beside me. I could feel his breath on my neck. "I can't see myself." He sounded very frightened.

"Don't get tense," I said, forcing myself to sound calm. "You know it takes a while. Especially since you stayed invisible so long."

"But how long?" Zack wailed. "Shouldn't I be back by now? *You* were back by now. I remember."

"Just stay cool," I told him, even though my stomach was churning and my throat was dry.

"This is too scary. I *hate* this!" April moaned.

"Be patient," I repeated softly. "Everybody just be patient."

We all stared from the spot where we thought Zack was standing to the mirror, then back again.

"Zack, how do you feel?" Erin asked, her voice trembling.

"Weird," Zack replied. "Like I'm never coming back."

"Don't say that!" I snapped.

"But that's how I feel," Zack said sadly. "Like I'm never coming back."

"Just chill," I said. "Everybody. Just chill."

We stood in silence. Watching. Waiting.

Waiting.

I was never so frightened in all my life.

11

"Do something!" Zack, still invisible, pleaded. "Max — you've *got* to do something!"

"I — I'd better get Mom," Lefty stammered. He dropped the softball to the floor and started to the door.

"Mom? What could Mom do?" I cried in a panic.

"But I'd better get *somebody*!" Lefty declared.

At that moment, Zack shimmered back into view. "Wow!" He uttered a long, breathless sigh of relief and slumped to his knees on the floor.

"Yaaaay!" Erin cried happily, clapping her hands as we all gathered around Zack.

"How do you feel?" I asked, grabbing his shoulders. I think I wanted to know for sure that he was really back.

"I'm back!" Zack proclaimed, smiling. "That's all I care about."

"That was really scary," April said quietly, hands shoved into the pockets of her white tennis shorts. "I mean, really."

"I wasn't scared," Zack said, suddenly changing his tune. "I knew there was no problem."

Do you *believe* this guy?

One second, he's whining and wailing, begging me to do something.

The next second, he's pretending he had the time of his life. Mister Confident.

"What did it feel like?" Erin asked, resting one hand on the wooden mirror frame.

"Awesome," Zack replied. He climbed unsteadily to his feet. "Really. It was totally awesome! I want to get invisible again before school on Monday so I can go spy in the girls' locker room!"

"Zack, you're a pig!" Erin declared disgustedly.

"What's the point of being invisible if you can't spy on girls?" Zack asked.

"Are you sure you're okay?" I asked, genuinely concerned. "You look kind of shaky to me."

"Well, I started to feel a little strange at the end," Zack confessed, scratching the back of his head.

"How do you mean?" I asked.

"Well, like I was being pulled away. Away from the room. Away from you guys."

"Pulled where?" I demanded.

He shrugged. "I don't know. I only know one thing." A smile began to form on his face, and his blue eyes seemed to light up.

Uh-oh, I thought.

"I only know one thing," Zack repeated.

"What?" I had to ask.

"I'm the new invisible champ. I stayed invisible longer than you. At least five minutes. Longer than anybody."

"But I haven't had a turn!" Erin protested.

"I don't *want* a turn!" April declared.

"Chicken?" Zack teased her.

"I think you're stupid for messing around with this," April said heatedly. "It isn't a toy, you know. You don't know anything about it. You don't know what it really does to your body."

"I feel fine!" Zack told her, and pounded his chest with both hands like a gorilla to prove it. He glanced at the dark mirror. "I'm ready to go back — even longer."

"I want to get invisible and go outside and play tricks on people," Lefty said enthusiastically. "Can I go next, Max?"

"I — I don't think so. . . ."

I was thinking about what April had said. We really were messing around with something that could be dangerous, something we didn't know anything about.

"Max has to go again," Zack said, slapping me hard on the back, nearly sending me sprawling against the mirror. "To beat my record." He grinned at me. "Unless you're chicken, too."

"I'm *not* chicken!" I insisted. "I just think — "

"You're chicken," Zack accused, laughing scornfully. He started clucking loudly, flapping his arms
like a chicken.

"*I'm* not chicken. Let *me* go," Lefty pleaded.
"I can break Zack's record."

"It's my turn," Erin insisted. "You guys have
all had turns. I haven't gone once yet!"

"Okay," I said with a shrug. "You go first, Erin.
Then me." I was glad Erin was so eager to do it.
I really didn't feel like getting invisible again just
yet.

To be honest, I felt very fluttery and nervous.

"Me next!" Lefty insisted. "Me next! Me next!"
He started chanting the words over and over.

I clamped my hand over his mouth. "Maybe we
should all go downstairs," I suggested.

"Chicken?" Zack teased. "You're chickening
out?"

"I don't know, Zack," I replied honestly. "I
think — " I saw Erin staring at me. Was that
disappointment on her face? Did Erin think I was
a chicken, too?

"Okay," I said. "Go ahead, Erin. You go. Then
I'll go. Then Lefty. We'll all beat Zack's record."

Erin and Lefty clapped. April groaned and
rolled her eyes. Zack grinned.

It's no big deal, I told myself. I've done it three
times already. It's perfectly painless. And if you
just stay cool and wait patiently, you come right
back the way you were.

"Does anyone have a watch?" Erin asked. "We need to keep time so I know what time I have to beat."

I could see that Erin was really into this competition.

Lefty seemed really excited, too. And of course Zack would compete in *anything*.

Only April was unhappy about the whole thing. She walked silently to the back of the room and sat down on the floor with her back against the wall, her arms folded over her knees.

"Hey, you're the only one with a watch," Erin called to April. "So you be the timer, okay?"

April nodded without enthusiasm. She raised her wrist and stared down at her watch. "Okay. Get ready."

Erin took a deep breath and stepped up to the mirror. She closed her eyes, reached up, and tugged the light chain.

The light came on with a bright flash. Erin disappeared.

"Oh, wow!" she cried. "This is way cool!"

"How does it feel?" April called from behind us, her eyes glancing from the mirror to her watch.

"I don't feel any different at all," Erin said. "What a great way to lose weight!"

"Fifteen seconds," April announced.

Lefty's hair suddenly stood straight up in the air. "Cut it out, Erin!" he shouted, twisting away from her invisible hands.

We heard Erin laugh from somewhere near Lefty.

Then we heard her footsteps as she walked out of the room and into the attic. We saw an old coat rise up into the air and dance around. After it dropped back into its carton, we saw an old magazine fly up and its pages appear to flip rapidly.

"This is so much fun!" Erin called to us. The magazine dropped back onto the stack. "I can't *wait* to go outside like this and really scare people!"

"One minute," April called. She hadn't moved from her sitting position against the wall.

Erin moved around the attic for a while, making things fly and float. Then she returned to the little room to admire herself in the mirror.

"I'm really invisible!" we heard her exclaim excitedly. "Just like in a movie or something!"

"Yeah. Great special effects!" I said.

"Three minutes," April announced.

Erin continued to enjoy herself until about four minutes had passed. Then her voice suddenly changed. She started to sound doubtful, frightened.

"I — I don't like this," she said. "I feel kind of strange."

April jumped to her feet and ran up to me. "Bring her back!" she demanded. "Hurry!"

I hesitated.

"Yes. Bring me back," Erin said weakly.

"But you haven't beaten my record!" Zack declared. "Are you sure — ?"

"Yes. Please. I don't feel right." Erin suddenly sounded far away.

I stepped up to the mirror and pulled the chain. The light clicked off.

We waited for Erin to return.

"How do you feel?" I asked.

"Just . . . weird," she replied. She was standing right next to me, but I still couldn't see her.

It took nearly three minutes for Erin to reappear. Three very tense minutes.

When she shimmered back into view, she shook herself like a dog shaking water off after a bath. Then she grinned at us reassuringly. "I'm okay. It was really terrific. Except for the last few seconds."

"You didn't beat my record," Zack reported happily. "You came so close. But you folded. Just like a girl."

"Hey — " Erin gave Zack a hard shove. "Stop being such a jerk."

"But you only had fifteen seconds to go, and you wimped out!" Zack told her.

"I don't care," Erin insisted, frowning angrily at him. "It was really neat. I'll beat your record next time, Zack."

"I'm going to be the winner," Lefty announced. "I'm going to stay invisible for a whole day. Maybe two!"

"Whoa!" I cried. "That might be dangerous, Lefty."

"It's Max's turn next," Zack announced. "Unless you want to forfeit."

"No way," I said, glancing at Erin. Reluctantly, I stepped up to the mirror and took a deep breath. "Okay, Zack, say good-bye to your record," I said, trying to sound calm and confident.

I didn't really want to do it, I admitted to myself. But I didn't want to look like a chicken in front of the others. For one thing, if I did wimp out, I knew that Lefty would only remind me of it twenty or thirty times a day for the rest of my life.

So I decided to go ahead and do it.

"One thing," I said to Zack. "When I call out 'ready,' that means I want to come back. So when I say 'ready,' you pull the light chain as fast as you can — okay?"

"Gotcha," Zack replied, his expression turning serious. "Don't worry. I'll bring you back instantly." He snapped his fingers. "Like that. Remember, Max, you've got to beat five minutes."

"Okay. Here goes," I said, staring at my reflection in the mirror.

I suddenly had a bad feeling about this.

A real bad feeling.

But I reached up and pulled on the light anyway.

12

When the glaring light dimmed, I stared hard into the mirror.

The reflections were bright and clear. Against the back wall, I could see April, slumped on the floor, staring intently at her watch.

Lefty stood near the wall to the right, gaping at the spot where I had stood, a silly grin on his face. Zack stood next to him, his arms crossed over his chest, also staring into the mirror. Erin leaned against the wall to the left. Her eyes were on the light above the mirror frame.

And where was I?

Standing right in front of the mirror. Right in the center of it. Staring at their reflections. Staring at the spot where my reflection should be.

Only it wasn't.

I felt perfectly normal.

Experimenting, I kicked the floor. My invisible sneakers made the usual scraping sound.

I grabbed my left arm with my right hand and

335

squeezed it. It felt perfectly normal.

"Hi, everyone," I said. I sounded the same as ever.

Only I was invisible.

I glanced up at the light, casting a yellow rectangle down onto the mirror. What was the light's power? I wondered.

Did it do something to your molecules? Make them break apart somehow so you couldn't be seen?

No. That wasn't a good theory. If your molecules broke up, you'd *have* to feel it. And you wouldn't be able to kick the floor, or squeeze your arm, or talk.

So what did the light do? Did it cover you up somehow? Did the light form some kind of blanket? A covering that hid you from yourself and everyone else?

What a mystery!

I had the feeling I'd never be able to figure it out, never know the answer.

I turned my eyes away from the light. It was starting to hurt my eyes.

I closed my eyes, but the bright glare stayed with me. Two white circles that refused to dim.

"How do you feel, Max?" Erin's voice broke into my thoughts.

"Okay, I guess," I said. My voice sounded weird to me, kind of far away.

"Four minutes, thirty seconds," April announced.

"The time went so fast," I said.

At least, I thought I said it. I realized I couldn't tell if I was saying the words or just thinking them.

The bright yellow light glowed even brighter.

I had the sudden feeling that it was pouring over me, surrounding me.

Pulling me.

"I — I feel weird," I said.

No response.

Could they hear me?

The light folded over me. I felt myself begin to float.

It was a frightening feeling. As if I were losing control of my body.

"Ready!" I screamed. "Zack — ready! Can you hear me, Zack?"

It seemed to take Zack hours to reply. "Okay," I heard him say. His voice sounded so tiny, so far away.

Miles and miles away.

"Ready!" I cried. "Ready!"

"Okay!" Again I heard Zack's voice.

But the light was so bright, so blindingly bright. Waves of yellow light rolling over me. Ocean waves of light.

Sweeping me away with it.

"Pull the chain, Zack!" I screamed. At least, I *think* I was screaming.

The light was tugging me so hard, dragging me away, far, far away.

I knew I would float away. Float forever.

Unless Zack pulled the chain and brought me back.

"Pull it! Pull it! *Please* — pull it!"

"Okay."

I saw Zack step up to the mirror.

He was blurred in shadows. He stepped through dark shadows, on the other side of the light.

So far away.

I felt so feather light.

I could see Zack in the shadows. He jumped up. He grabbed the lamp chain.

He pulled it down hard.

The light didn't click off. It glowed even brighter.

And then I saw Zack's face fill with horror.

He held up his hand. He was trying to show me something.

He had the chain in his hand.

"Max, the chain — " he stammered. "It broke off. I can't turn off the light!"

13

Beyond the shimmering wall of yellow light, Zack's outstretched hand came clearly into my view. The dark chain dangled from his hand like a dead snake.

"It broke off!" he was crying, sounding very alarmed.

I stared through the light at the chain, feeling myself hovering beside Zack, floating, fading.

Somewhere far in the distance, April was screaming. I couldn't make out her words.

Lefty stood frozen in the center of the room. It seemed strange to see him standing so still. He was always moving, always bouncing, running, falling. But now he, too, stood staring at the chain.

The light shimmered brighter.

I saw sudden movement.

Someone was crossing the room. I struggled to focus.

It was Erin. She was dragging a large cardboard box across the floor. The scraping sound it made seemed so far away.

Feeling myself being pulled away, I struggled to watch her. She pulled the box next to the mirror. Then she climbed up onto it.

I saw her reaching up to the lamp. I saw her staring into the light.

I wanted to ask her what she was doing, but I was too far away. I was floating off. I felt so light, so feather light.

And as I floated, the yellow light spread over me. It covered me. Pulled me.

And then with startling suddenness, it was gone.

And all was darkness.

"I did it!" Erin proclaimed.

I heard her explaining to the others. "There was a little bit of chain left up there. I pulled it and turned off the light." Her eyes darted frantically around the room, searching for me. "Max — are you okay? Can you hear me?"

"Yeah. I'm okay," I replied.

I felt better. Stronger. Closer.

I stepped up to the mirror and searched for my reflection.

"That was scary," Lefty said behind me.

"I can feel myself coming back," I told them.

"What was his time?" Zack asked April.

April's features were tight with worry. Sitting

against the wall, she looked pale and uncomfortable. "Five forty-eight," she told Zack. And then quickly added, "I really think this stupid competition is a big mistake."

"You beat my record!" Zack groaned, turning to where he figured I was standing. "I don't believe it! Almost six minutes!"

"I'm going for longer than that," Lefty said, pushing past Zack and stepping up to the mirror.

"We have to fix the chain first," Erin told him. "It's too hard to keep climbing up on a box to pull that little piece of chain."

"I felt pretty strange at the end," I told them, still waiting to reappear. "The light grew brighter and brighter."

"Did you feel like you were being pulled away?" Erin asked.

"Yeah," I replied. "Like I was fading or something."

"That's how *I* started to feel," Erin cried.

"This is just so dangerous," April said, shaking her head.

I popped back.

My knees buckled and I almost fell to the floor. But I grabbed the mirror and held myself up. After a few seconds, my legs felt strong again. I took a few steps and regained my balance.

"What if we couldn't turn off the light?" April demanded, climbing to her feet, brushing the dust off the back of her jeans with both hands. "What if the chain completely broke and the light stayed on? What then?"

I shrugged. "I don't know."

"You broke my record," Zack said, making a disgusted face. "That means I have to have another turn."

"No way!" Lefty shouted. "It's my turn next!"

"None of you are listening to me!" April cried. "Answer my question. What if one of you is invisible and the light won't go out?"

"That won't happen," Zack told her. He pulled a string from his pocket. "Here. I'm going to tie this tightly to the chain." He climbed up onto the box and began to work. "Pull the string. The light goes out," he told April. "No problem."

"Which one of us is going to be first to get invisible and then go outside?" Erin asked.

"I want to go to school and terrorize Miss Hawkins," Lefty said, snickering. Miss Hawkins is his social studies teacher. "She's been terrorizing me ever since school started. Wouldn't it be cool just to sneak up behind her and say, 'Hi, Miss Hawkins'? And she'd turn around and there'd be no one there?"

"That's the best you can do?" Erin scoffed. "Lefty, where's your imagination? Don't you want to make the chalk fly out of her hand, and the chalkboard erasers fly across the room, and the wastebasket spill everything out on her desk, and her yogurt fly into her face?"

"Yeah! That's way cool!" Lefty exclaimed.

I laughed. It was a funny idea. The four of us could go around, completely invisible, doing whatever we wanted. We could wreck the whole school in ten minutes! Everyone would be screaming and running out the doors. What a goof!

"We can't do it now," Lefty said, interrupting my thoughts. "Because it's my turn to beat the record." He turned back to April, who was standing tensely by the door, pulling at a strand of her black hair, a worried frown on her face. "Ready to time me?"

"I guess," she replied, sighing.

Lefty pushed me out of the way. He stepped in front of the mirror, stared at his reflection, an reached for the string.

14

"Lefty!" a voice shouted from behind us. "Lefty!"

Startled by the interruption, I uttered an alarmed cry. Lefty stepped back from the mirror.

"Lefty, tell your brother his friends have to leave! It's dinnertime. Grammy and Poppy are here. They're eager to see you!"

It was Mom, calling up from downstairs.

"Okay, Mom. We'll be right down!" I shouted quickly. I didn't want her to come up.

"But that's not *fair!*" Lefty whined. "I didn't get my turn."

He stepped back up to the mirror and angrily grabbed for the string again.

"Put it down," I told him sternly. "We have to go downstairs. Quick. We don't want Mom or Dad coming up here and seeing the mirror, do we?"

"Okay, okay," Lefty grumbled. "But next time, I get to go first."

"And then me," Zack said, heading toward the stairs. "I get a chance to beat your record, Max."

"Everybody, stop talking about it," I warned as we all clomped down the stairs. "Talk about something else. We don't want them to overhear anything."

"Can we come over tomorrow?" Erin asked. "We could start up the contest again."

"I'm busy tomorrow," April said.

"We can't do it tomorrow," I replied. "We're visiting my cousins in Springfield." I was sorry they'd reminded me. My cousins have this humongous sheepdog that likes to run through the mud and then jump on me and wipe its hairy paws all over my clothes. Not my idea of a good time.

"There's no school on Wednesday," Zack said. "Teachers' meetings, I think. Maybe we could all come over on Wednesday."

"Maybe," I said.

We stepped into the hallway. Everyone stopped talking. I could see that my grandparents and parents were already sitting at the dining room table. Grammy and Poppy liked to eat promptly. If their dinner came one minute late, it made them real cranky for the rest of the day.

I ushered my friends out quickly, reminding them not to tell anyone about what we'd been doing. Zack asked again if Wednesday would be okay, and again I told him I wasn't sure.

Getting invisible was really exciting, really thrilling. But it also made me nervous. I wasn't sure I wanted to do it again so soon.

"Please!" Zack begged. He couldn't wait to get invisible again and beat my record. He couldn't stand it that he wasn't the champ.

I closed the front door behind them and hurried to the dining room to greet my grandparents. They were already slurping their soup when I came in.

"Hi, Grammy. Hi, Poppy." I walked around the table and gave them each a kiss on the cheek. Grammy smelled of oranges. Her cheek felt soft and mushy.

Grammy and Poppy are the names I gave them when I was a kid. It's really embarrassing to call them that now, but I still do. I don't have much choice. They even call *each other* Grammy and Poppy!

They look alike, almost like brother and sister. I guess that's what happens when you've been married a hundred years. They both have long, thin faces and short white hair. They both wear thick glasses with silver wire frames. They're both really skinny. And they both have sad eyes and sad expressions.

I didn't feel like sitting there at dinner and making small talk with them today. I was still really pumped about what we'd been doing all afternoon.

Being invisible was just so weird and exciting.

I wanted to be by myself and think about it. You know. Try to relive it, relive what it felt like.

A lot of times after I've done something really exciting or interesting, I like to go up to my room, lie down on my bed, and just think about it. Analyze it. Tear it apart.

Dad says I have a very scientific mind. I guess he's right.

I walked over to my place at the table.

"You're looking much shorter," Poppy said, wiping his mouth with his cloth napkin. That was one of his standard jokes. He said it every time he saw me.

I forced a laugh and sat down.

"Your soup must be ice cold by now," Grammy said, clicking her tongue. "Nothing I hate more than cold soup. I mean, what's the point of having soup if it isn't steaming hot?"

"It tastes okay," I said, taking a spoonful.

"We had some delicious cold soup last summer," Poppy said. He loved to contradict Grammy and start arguments with her. "Strawberry soup, remember? You wouldn't want *that* hot, would you?"

"It wasn't strawberry," Grammy told him, frowning. "It wasn't even soup. It was some kind of fancy yogurt."

"No, it wasn't," Poppy insisted. "It was definitely cold soup."

"You're wrong, as usual," Grammy snapped.

This could get ugly, I thought. "What kind of

soup is this?" I asked, trying to stop their arguing.

"Chicken noodle," Mom answered quickly. "Didn't you recognize it?"

"Poppy and I had soup a few weeks ago that we couldn't recognize," my grandmother said, shaking her head. "I had to ask the waiter what it was. It didn't look like what we'd ordered at all. Some kind of potato-leek soup, wasn't it, Poppy?"

Poppy took a long time swallowing some noodles. "No. Tomato," he answered.

"Where's your brother?" Dad asked, staring at the empty chair next to me.

"Huh?" I reacted with surprise. I had been so busy listening to my grandparents' silly soup arguments, I had forgotten all about Lefty.

"His soup is getting cold," Poppy said.

"You'll have to heat it up for him," Grammy said, tsk-tsking again.

"So where is he?" Dad asked.

I shrugged. "He was right behind me," I said. I turned toward the dining room doorway and shouted, "Lefty! *Lef-teeeee!*"

"Don't shout at the table," Mom scolded. "Get up and go find him."

"Is there any more soup?" Poppy asked. "I didn't really get enough."

I put my napkin down and started to get up. But before I was out of my chair, I saw Lefty's soup bowl rise up into the air.

Oh, no! I thought.

I knew instantly what was happening.

My idiot brother had made himself invisible, and now he thought he was being funny, trying to scare the daylights out of everyone at the table.

The soup bowl floated up over Lefty's place.

I stood up and lunged for it and pulled it down as fast as I could.

"Get out!" I whispered loudly to Lefty.

"What did you say?" my mom asked, gaping at me.

"I said I'm getting out and going to find Lefty," I told her, thinking quickly.

"Get out — now!" I whispered to Lefty.

"Stop talking about finding him. Just go do it," my mom said impatiently.

I stood up just as my dumb invisible brother raised his water glass. The glass floated up over the table.

I gasped and grabbed for it.

But I grabbed too hard. I jerked the glass, and water spilled all over the table.

"Hey!" Mom screamed.

I pulled the glass down to its place.

Then I looked up. Dad was glaring at me, his eyes burning angrily into mine.

He knows, I thought, a heavy feeling of dread sweeping over me.

He saw what just happened, and he knows.

Lefty has spoiled it for everyone.

15

Dad glared angrily across the table at me.

I waited for him to say, "Max, why is your brother invisible?" But instead, he yelled, "Stop fooling around, Max. We don't appreciate your comedy act. Just get up and find your brother."

I was so relieved. Dad hadn't realized what was really happening, after all. He thought I was just goofing.

"Is there seconds on the soup?" I heard Poppy ask again as I gratefully pushed away from the table and hurried out of the dining room.

"You've had enough," Grammy scolded.

"No, I haven't!"

I made my way quickly through the living room, taking long strides, climbed to the second floor, and stopped in the hallway at the door to the attic stairs. "Lefty?" I whispered. "I hope you followed me."

"I'm here," Lefty whispered back. I couldn't see him, of course, but he was right beside me.

"What's the big idea?" I demanded angrily. I wasn't angry. I was *furious*. "Are you trying to win the *stupid* championship?"

Lefty didn't care that I was upset. He started to giggle.

"Shut up!" I whispered. "Just shut up! You really are a dork!"

I clicked on the attic light and clomped angrily up the stairs. I could hear his sneakers clomping up behind mine.

He was still giggling at the top of the stairs. "I win!" he declared. I felt a hand slap me hard on the back.

"Stop it, jerk!" I screamed, storming into the little room that housed the mirror. "Don't you realize you nearly spoiled it for everybody?"

"But I win!" he repeated gleefully.

The lamp over the mirror was shining brightly, the reflection glaring sun-yellow in the mirror.

I really couldn't believe Lefty. He was usually a pretty selfish kid. But not *this* selfish!

"Don't you realize the trouble you could have gotten us into?" I cried.

"I win! I win!" he chanted.

"Why? How long have you been invisible?" I asked. I stepped up to the mirror and pulled the string. The light went out. The glare remained in my eyes.

"Ever since you guys went downstairs," Lefty, still invisible, bragged.

"That's almost ten minutes!" I exclaimed.

"I'm the champ!" Lefty proclaimed.

I stared into the mirror, waiting for him to re-appear.

"The stupidity champ," I repeated. "This was the dumbest thing you've ever done."

He didn't say anything. Finally, he asked in a quiet voice, "Why is it taking so long for me to come back?"

Before I could answer, I heard Dad calling from downstairs: "Max? Are you two up there?"

"Yeah. We'll be right down," I shouted.

"What are you two *doing* up there?" Dad demanded. I heard him start to climb the stairs.

I ran to the top of the stairs to head him off. "Sorry, Dad," I said. "We're coming."

Dad stared up at me in the stairwell. "What on earth is so interesting up there?"

"Just a lot of old stuff," I muttered. "Nothing, really."

Lefty appeared behind me, looking like his old self. Dad disappeared back to the dining room. Lefty and I started down the stairs.

"Wow, that was *awesome*!" Lefty exclaimed.

"Didn't you start to feel weird after a while?" I asked him, whispering even though we were alone.

"No." He shook his head. "I felt fine. It was really *awesome*! You should have seen the look on your face when I made the soup bowl float up in the air!" He started giggling again, that high-pitched giggle of his that I hate.

"Listen, Lefty," I warned, stopping at the bottom of the stairs, blocking his way to the hallway. "Getting invisible is fun, but it could be dangerous. You — "

"It's awesome!" he repeated. "And I'm the new champ."

"Listen to me," I said heatedly, grabbing him by the shoulders. "Just listen. You've got to promise me that you won't go up there and get invisible by yourself again. I mean it. You've got to wait till someone else is around. Promise?" I squeezed his shoulders hard.

"Okay, okay," he said, trying to squirm away. "I promise."

I looked down. He had his fingers crossed on both hands.

Erin called me later that night. It was about eleven. I was in my pajamas, reading a book in bed, thinking about going downstairs and begging my parents to let me stay up and watch *Saturday Night Live*.

Erin sounded really excited. She didn't even say hello. Just started talking a mile a minute in that squeaky mouse voice, so fast I had trouble understanding her.

"What about the science fair?" I asked, holding the phone away from my ear, hoping that would help me understand her better.

"The winning project," Erin said breathlessly. "The prize is a silver trophy and a gift certificate at Video World. Remember?"

"Yeah. So?" I still wasn't following her. I think I was sleepier than I'd thought. It had been a nervous, tiring day, after all.

"Well, what if you brought the mirror to school?" Erin asked excitedly. "You know. I would make you go invisible. Then I'd bring you back, and I'd get invisible. That could be our project."

"But, Erin — " I started to protest.

"We'd win!" she interrupted. "We'd *have* to win! I mean, what else could beat it? We'd win first prize. And we'd be famous!"

"Whoa!" I cried. "Famous?"

"Of course. Famous!" she exclaimed. "Our picture would be in *People* magazine and everything!"

"Erin, I'm not so sure about this," I said softly, thinking hard.

"Huh? Not so sure about *what*?"

"Not so sure I want to be famous," I replied. "I mean, I really don't know if I want the whole world to know about the mirror."

"Why not?" she demanded impatiently. "*Everyone* wants to be famous. And rich."

"But they'll take away the mirror," I explained. "It's an amazing thing, Erin. I mean, is it magic? Is it electronic? Is it someone's invention? Whatever it is, it's unbelievable! And they're not going to let a kid keep it."

"But it's *yours*!" she insisted.

"They'll take it away to study it. Scientists will want it. Government guys will want it. Army guys. They'll probably want to use it to make the army invisible or something."

"Scary," Erin mumbled thoughtfully.

"Yeah. Scary," I said. "So I don't know. I've got to think about this. A lot. In the meantime, it's got to be a secret."

"Yeah, I guess," she said doubtfully. "But think about the science fair, Max. We could win the prize. We really could."

"I'll think about it," I told her.

I haven't thought about anything else! I realized.

"April wants to try it," she said.

"Huh?"

"I convinced her. I told her it didn't hurt or anything. So she wants to try it on Wednesday. We *are* going to do it on Wednesday, aren't we, Max?"

"I guess," I replied reluctantly. "Since everyone wants to."

"Great!" she exclaimed. "I think I'll beat your record."

"The new record is ten minutes," I informed her. I explained about Lefty and his dinnertime adventure.

"Your brother is really a nut," Erin remarked.

I agreed with her, then said good night.

I couldn't get to sleep that night. I tried sleeping on one side, then the other. I tried counting sheep. Everything.

I knew I was sleepy. But my heart was racing. I just couldn't get comfortable. I stared up at the ceiling, thinking about the mirror in the little room above me.

It was nearly three in the morning when I crept barefoot out of my room, wide awake, and headed up to the attic. As before, I leaned heavily on the banister as I climbed, trying to keep the wooden stairs from their usual symphony of creaks and groans.

In my hurry to get to the little room, I stubbed my toe on the corner of a wooden crate.

"Ow!" I screamed as quietly as possible. I wanted to hop up and down, but I forced myself to stand still, and waited for the pain to fade.

As soon as I could walk again, I made my way into the little room. I pulled a carton in front of the mirror and sat down on it.

My toe still throbbed, but I tried to ignore it. I stared at my dark reflection in the mirror, studying my hair first, of course. It was totally messed up, but I really didn't care.

Then I peered beyond my reflection, behind it. I guess I was trying to look deep into the glass. I don't really know what I was doing or why I was up there.

I was so tired and pumped up at the same time, so curious and confused, sleepy and nervous.

I ran a hand along the glass, surprised again at how cool it felt in the hot, nearly airless little room. I pushed my open hand against the glass, then pulled it away. It left no handprint.

I moved my hand to the wooden frame, once again rubbing the smooth wood. I stood up and slowly walked around to the back of the mirror. It was too dark back here to really examine it carefully. But there wasn't anything to examine. The back of the frame was smooth, plain, and uninteresting.

I came back around to the front and gazed up at the light. It looked like an ordinary lamp. Nothing at all special about it. The bulb was an odd shape, long and very thin. But it looked like an ordinary light bulb.

Sitting back down on the carton, I rested my head in my hands and stared drowsily into the mirror. I yawned silently.

I knew I should go back downstairs and go to sleep. Mom and Dad were going to wake us up early the next morning to drive to Springfield.

But something was holding me there.

My curiosity, I guess.

357

I don't know how long I sat there, still as a statue, watching my own unmoving reflection. It may have been just a minute or two. Or it might have been half an hour.

But after a while, as I stared into the mirror, the reflection seemed to lose its sharpness. Now I found myself staring at vague shapes, blurred colors, deepening shadows.

And then I heard the soft whisper.

"Maaaaaaaax."

Like the wind through the trees. The hushed shaking of leaves.

Not a voice at all. Not even a whisper.

Just the hint of a whisper.

"Maaaaaaaaax."

At first, I thought it was inside my own head. So faint. So soft. But so near.

I held my breath, listened hard.

Silence now.

So it *was* inside my head, I told myself. I *was* imagining it.

I took a deep breath, let it out slowly.

"Maaaaax."

Again, the whisper.

Louder this time. Sad, somehow. Almost a plea. A call for help. From far, far away.

"Maaaaaaaax."

I raised my hands to my ears. Was I trying to shut it out? To see if I could make it go away?

Inside the mirror, the dark reflected shapes

shifted slowly. I stared back at myself, my expression tense, frightened. I realized I was chilled from head to foot. My whole body shivered from the cold.

"*Maaaaax.*"

The whisper, I realized, was coming from the mirror.

From my own reflection? From somewhere behind my reflection?

I leapt to my feet, turned away, and ran. My bare feet slapped against the hardwood floor. I plunged down the stairs, flew across the hall, dived into my bed.

I shut my eyes tight and prayed the frightening whisper wouldn't follow me.

16

I pulled the covers up to my chin. I felt so cold. My entire body was trembling.

I was breathing hard, gripping the top of the blanket with both hands, waiting, listening.

Would the whispers follow me into my room? Were they real, or only in my head?

Who was calling to me, whispering my name in that sad, desperate voice?

Suddenly I heard panting louder than mine. I felt hot breath on my face. Sour-smelling and moist.

It reached for me. It grabbed my face.

I opened my eyes in terror.

"Whitey!" I cried.

The dumb dog was standing on his hind paws, leaning over the blanket, furiously licking my face.

"Whitey, good dog!" I cried, laughing. His

scratchy tongue tickled. I was never so glad to see him.

I hugged him and pulled him up into the bed. He whimpered excitedly. His tail was wagging like crazy.

"Whitey, what's got you so worked up?" I asked, hugging him. "Do you hear voices, too?"

He uttered a low bark, as if answering the question. Then he hopped off the bed and shook himself. He turned three times in a tight circle, making a place for himself on the carpet, and lay down, yawning loudly.

"You're definitely weird tonight," I said. He curled himself into a tight ball and chewed softly on his tail.

Accompanied by the dog's gentle snores, I eventually drifted into a restless sleep.

When I awoke, the morning sky outside my bedroom window was still gray. The window was open just a crack, and the curtains were swaying in a strong breeze.

I sat up quickly, instantly alert. I have to stop going up to the attic, I thought.

I have to forget about the stupid mirror.

I stood up and stretched. I've got to stop. And I've got to get everyone else to stop.

I thought of the whispered cry from the night before. The dry, sad voice, whispering my name.

"Max!"

The voice from outside my room startled me out of my chilling thoughts.

"Max — time to wake up! We're going to Springfield, remember?" It was my mom out in the hallway. "Hurry. Breakfast is on the table."

"I'm already up!" I shouted. "I'll be down in a minute."

I heard her footsteps going down the stairs. Then I heard Whitey downstairs barking at the door to be let out.

I stretched again.

"Whoa!" I cried out as my closet door swung open.

A red Gap T-shirt rose up off the top shelf and began to float across the room.

I heard giggling. Familiar giggling.

The T-shirt danced in front of me.

"Lefty, you're ridiculous!" I yelled angrily. I swiped at the T-shirt, but it danced out of my reach. "You promised you wouldn't do this again!"

"I had my fingers crossed," he said, giggling.

"I don't care!" I cried. I lunged forward and grabbed the shirt. "You've got to stop. I mean it."

"I just wanted to surprise you," he said, pretending his feelings were hurt. A pair of jeans floated up from the closet shelf and began to parade back and forth in front of me.

"Lefty, I'm going to *murder* you!" I shouted. Then I lowered my voice, remembering that Mom and Dad might hear. "Put that down — now. Go upstairs and turn off the mirror light. Hurry!"

I shook my fist at where the jeans were marching. I was so angry.

Why did he have to be so dumb? Didn't he realize that this wasn't just a game?

Suddenly, the jeans collapsed in a heap on the carpet.

"Lefty, toss them to me," I instructed him. "Then get upstairs and get yourself visible again."

Silence.

The jeans didn't move.

"Lefty— don't fool around," I snapped, feeling a stab of dread in the pit of my stomach. "Toss me the jeans and get out of here."

No reply.

The jeans remained crumpled on the carpet.

"Stop this stupid game!" I screamed. "You're not funny! So just stop it. Really. You're *scaring* me!"

I knew that's what he wanted to hear. Once I admitted that he was scaring me, I was sure he'd giggle and go do as I said.

But no. The room was still silent. The curtains fluttered toward me, then pulled back with a gentle rustling sound. The jeans lay crumpled on the carpet.

"Lefty? Hey, Lefty?" I called, my voice trembling.

No reply.

"Lefty? Are you here?"

No.

Lefty was gone.

17

"Lefty?" My voice came out weak and trembling.

He wasn't there. It wasn't a game. He was gone.

Without thinking, I ran out of my room, down the hall, and up the stairs to the attic. My bare feet pounded on the steep wooden steps. My heart was pounding even louder.

As I stepped into the heat of the attic, a wave of fear swept over me.

What if Lefty had disappeared *forever*?

With a frightened cry, I lunged into the tiny room.

The bright light reflected in the mirror shone into my eyes.

Shielding my eyes with one hand, I made my way to the mirror and pulled the string. The light went out immediately.

"Lefty?" I called anxiously.

No reply.

"Lefty? Are you up here? Can you hear me?"

Fear clogged my throat. I was panting loudly, barely able to speak.

"Lefty?"

"Hi, Max. I'm here." My brother's voice came from right beside me.

I was so happy to hear it, I turned and gave him a hug, even though I couldn't see him.

"I'm okay," he said, startled by my emotion. "Really, Max. I'm okay."

It took a few minutes for him to reappear.

"What happened?" I asked, checking him out, looking him up and down as if I hadn't seen him for months. "You were clowning around in my room. Then you were gone."

"I'm fine," he insisted with a shrug.

"But where did you go?" I demanded.

"Up here," he repeated.

"But Lefty — " Something about him looked different. I couldn't quite put my finger on it. But staring at his face, I was sure that something was weird.

"Stop staring at me like that, Max." He shoved me away. "I'm fine. Really." He started dancing away from me, heading to the stairs.

"But, Lefty — " I followed him out of the room.

"No more questions. Okay? I'm all right."

"Stay away from the mirror," I said sternly. "Do you hear me?"

He started down the stairs.

"I mean it, Lefty. Don't get invisible again."

"Okay, okay," he snapped. "I won't do it anymore."

I checked to make sure his fingers weren't crossed. This time they weren't.

Mom was waiting for us in the hall. "So *there* you are," she said impatiently. "Max, you're not dressed!"

"I'll hurry," I told her, and bolted into my room.

"Lefty, what did you do to your hair?" I heard Mom ask my brother. "Did you brush it differently or something?"

"No," I heard Lefty reply. "It's the same, Mom. Really. Maybe your eyes are different."

"Stop being such a smart mouth and get downstairs," Mom told him.

Something was definitely weird about Lefty. Mom had noticed it, too. But I couldn't figure out what.

As I picked my jeans up off the floor and pulled them on, I started to feel a little better. I had been so frightened, frightened that something terrible had happened to my brother. Frightened that he'd disappeared for good, and I'd never see him again.

All because of that stupid mirror.

All because it was such a thrill to get invisible.

I suddenly thought about Erin, April, and Zack.

They were so excited about Wednesday. About the big competition. Even April was going to get invisible this time.

No, I thought.

I have to call them. I have to tell them.

I've really made up my mind.

No more mirror. No more getting invisible.

I'll call all three of them when I get back from Springfield. And I'll tell them the competition is cancelled.

I sat down on my bed to tie my sneakers.

Whew, I thought. That's a load off my mind.

And it was. Having decided not to use the mirror ever again made me feel much, much better. All of my fear seemed to float away.

Little did I know that the most frightening time was still to come.

18

Imagine my surprise when Zack, Erin, and April showed up at my front door on Wednesday morning.

"I told you guys the competition is off," I sputtered, staring at them in astonishment through the screen door.

"But Lefty called us," Erin replied. "He said you changed your mind." The other two agreed.

My mouth dropped open to my knees. "Lefty?"

They nodded. "He called us yesterday," April said.

"But Lefty isn't even here this morning," I told them as they marched into the house. "He's at the playground playing softball with some of his friends."

"Who's here?" my mom called. She came walking into the hallway, drying her hands on a dish towel. She recognized my friends, then turned to me, a bewildered look on her face. "Max, I thought you were going to help me down in the basement.

369

I didn't know you'd made plans with Zack, Erin, and April."

"I didn't," I replied weakly. "Lefty — "

"We just dropped by," Zack told Mom, coming to my rescue.

"If you're busy, Max, we can go," Erin added.

"No, that's okay," Mom told them. "Max was complaining about how boring it would be to help me. It's good you three showed up."

She disappeared back into the kitchen. As soon as she was gone, my three friends practically pounced on me.

"Upstairs!" Zack cried eagerly, pointing to the stairs.

"Let's get invisible!" Erin whispered.

"I get to go first since I've never gone," April said.

I tried to argue with them, but I was outnumbered and outvoted. "Okay, okay," I reluctantly agreed. I started to follow them up the stairs when I heard scratching noises at the door.

I recognized the sound. It was Whitey, back from his morning walk. I pushed open the screen door and he trotted in, wagging his tail.

The dumb dog had some burrs stuck to his tail. I chased him into the kitchen and managed to get him to stand still long enough to pull them off. Then I hurried up to the attic to join my friends.

By the time I got up there, April was already standing in front of the mirror, and Zack was standing beside her, ready to pull the light on.

"Whoa!" I called.

They turned to look at me. I could see that April had a frightened expression on her face. "I have to do this right away. Or else I might wimp out," she explained.

"I just think we should get the rules straight first," I said sternly. "This mirror really isn't a toy, and — "

"We know, we know," Zack interrupted, grinning. "Come on, Max. No lectures today, okay? We know you're nervous because you're going to lose. But that's no reason — "

"I don't want to compete," April said nervously. "I just want to see what it's like to be invisible. For just a minute. Then I want to come back."

"Well, I'm going for the world's record," Zack boasted, leaning against the mirror frame.

"Me, too," Erin said.

"I really don't think it's a good idea," I told them, staring at my reflection in the mirror. "We should just get invisible for a short time. It's too dangerous to — "

"What a wimp!" Zack declared, shaking his head.

"We'll be careful, Max," Erin said.

"I just have a really bad feeling," I confessed. My hair was standing up in the back. I stepped closer to the mirror to see better, and smoothed it down with my hand.

"I think we should all get invisible at the same time," Zack said to me, his blue eyes lighting up with excitement. "Then we could go to the playground and scare your brother to death!"

Everyone laughed except April. "I just want to try it for a minute," she insisted. "That's all."

"First we compete," Erin told Zack. "Then we go out and scare people."

"Yeah! All *right*!" Zack exclaimed.

I decided to give up. There was no sense in trying to reason with Zack and Erin. They were too psyched for this competition. "Okay, let's get it over with," I told them.

"But first I go," April said, turning back to the mirror.

Zack reached up for the string again. "Ready? On three," he said.

I turned to the door as Whitey came sniffing his way in, his nose lowered to the floor, his tail straight out behind him.

"Whitey, what are *you* doing up here?" I asked.

He ignored me and continued sniffing furiously.

"One . . . two . . ." Zack started.

"When I say 'ready,' bring me back. Okay?" April asked, standing stiffly, staring straight ahead into the mirror. "No jokes or anything, Zack."

"No jokes," Zack replied seriously. "As soon as you want to come back, I'll turn off the light."

"Good," April replied softly.

Zack began his count again. "One . . . two . . . three!"

As he said three and pulled the string, Whitey stepped up beside April.

The light flashed on.

"Whitey!" I screamed. "Stop!"

But it was too late.

With a *yelp* of surprise, the dog vanished along with April.

19

"The dog!" Erin screamed.

"Hey — I'm gone! I'm invisible!" April exclaimed at the same time.

I could hear Whitey whimpering. He sounded really frightened.

"Pull the string!" I shouted to Zack.

"Not yet!" April protested.

"Pull it!" I insisted.

Zack pulled the string. The light went out. April reappeared first, with an angry expression on her face.

Whitey reappeared, and fell down. He jumped up quickly, but his legs were all wobbly.

He looked so funny, we all started to laugh.

"What's going on up there?" My mom's voice from the stairwell startled us into instant silence. "What are you doing?"

"Nothing, Mom," I answered quickly, signalling for my friends to remain silent. "Just hanging out."

"I don't understand what's so interesting up there in that dusty old attic," she called up.

I crossed my fingers, hoping she wouldn't come upstairs to find out.

"We just like it up here," I replied. Pretty lame, but it was the only thing I could think of to say.

Whitey, having recovered his balance, went running to the stairs. I heard the dog's toenails click on the wooden stairs as he went down to join my mom.

"That wasn't fair," April complained after Mom and Whitey were gone. "I didn't get any time."

"I think we should get out of here," I pleaded. "You see how unpredictable it is. You never know what's going to happen."

"That's sort of the fun of it," Erin insisted.

"I want another turn," April said.

We argued for about ten minutes. Once again, I lost.

It was time to start the competition. Erin was going first.

"Ten minutes is the time to beat," Zack instructed her.

"No problem," Erin said, making funny faces at herself in the mirror. "Ten minutes is too easy."

April had resumed her position, sitting on the floor with her back against the wall, studying her watch. We had agreed that she would take another turn after the competition was over.

After it was over . . .

375

Standing there watching Erin get ready, I wished it were over already. I felt cold all over. I had a heavy feeling of dread weighing me down.

Please, please, I thought to myself, let everything go okay.

Zack pulled the string.

Erin disappeared in the flash of light.

April studied her watch.

Zack took a step back from the mirror and crossed his arms in front of his chest. His eyes glowed with excitement.

"How do I look?" Erin teased.

"You never looked better," Zack joked.

"I like what you did with your hair," April teased, glancing up from the watch.

Even April was joking and having a good time. Why couldn't I relax, too? Why was I suddenly so frightened?

"You feel okay?" I asked Erin. The words nearly caught in my throat.

"Fine," Erin replied.

I could hear her footsteps as she walked around the room.

"If you start to feel weird, just say 'ready,' and Zack'll pull the string," I said.

"I know," she replied impatiently. "But I won't be ready to come back until I break the record."

"I'm going next," Zack told Erin, arms still crossed in front of him. "So your record won't last for long."

Suddenly Zack's arms uncrossed. His hands flew wildly up in the air, and he began slapping his face with both hands.

"Ow! Cut it out, Erin!" he yelled, trying to squirm away. "Let go!"

We heard Erin laugh as Zack slapped himself a few more times, then finally managed to wrestle out of her grip.

"One minute," April announced from behind us.

"Ow! You hurt me!" Zack said, scowling and rubbing his red cheeks.

Erin laughed again.

"You still feel okay?" I asked, glancing into the mirror.

"Fine. Stop worrying, Max," Erin scolded.

My T-shirt suddenly pulled up over my head. Erin laughed.

"Give me a break!" I cried, spinning away.

"Two minutes," April announced.

I heard the attic stairs creaking. A few seconds later, Whitey poked his head in. This time, he stopped in the doorway and peered into the room without entering.

"Go back downstairs, boy," I told him. "Go down."

He stared back at me as if considering my request. But he didn't budge from the doorway.

I didn't want to take another chance of him getting too close to the mirror. So I grabbed him by the collar and guided him to the stairs. Then it took a while for the dumb dog to get the idea that he was supposed to go *down* the stairs!

When I returned to the little room, April had just called out four minutes. Zack was pacing impatiently back and forth in front of the mirror. I guess he couldn't wait for it to be his turn.

I found myself thinking about Lefty. Lefty knew I had called everyone and canceled the competition. So why had he called Zack, Erin, and April and told them it was back on?

Just one of his practical jokes, I decided.

I'd have to find a way to pay him back for this. Something really evil . . .

"Eight minutes," April said, stretching.

"Pretty good," Zack told Erin. "Sure you don't want to quit now? There's no way you can win. Why not save everyone the time?"

"Do you still feel okay?" I asked anxiously.

No reply.

"Erin?" I called, searching around as if I had a chance of spotting her. "You feel okay?"

No reply.

"Erin — don't mess around. It's not funny!" I cried.

"Yeah. Answer us!" Zack demanded.

Still no reply.

Glancing into the mirror, I saw April's reflection, caught her horrified expression. "Erin's gone," she uttered, her voice a frightened whisper.

20

"Erin — where *are* you?" I shouted.

When she didn't reply, I ran over to the string. Just as I grabbed it, I heard footsteps outside the room. A few seconds later, a can of Coke came floating through the door.

"Miss me?" Erin asked playfully.

"You scared us to death!" I cried, my voice squeaking.

Erin laughed. "I didn't know you cared."

"That wasn't funny, Erin," Zack said sternly. For once he was agreeing with me. "You really did scare us."

"I got thirsty," Erin replied. The Coke can tilted up. We saw Coke start to pour out of it. The liquid abruptly disappeared as it flowed into Erin's mouth.

"I guess being invisible makes you really thirsty," Erin explained. "So I slipped downstairs and got a Coke."

"But you should've told us," April scolded, her

eyes turned back to her watch. "Nine minutes."

"You shouldn't go downstairs," I added heatedly. "I mean, what if my mom saw you?"

"*Saw* me?"

"Well . . . you know what I mean," I muttered. Erin laughed. I didn't think it was funny.

Why was I the only one taking this seriously?

Erin beat Lefty's record and kept going. When April called out twelve minutes, Zack asked Erin if she wanted to come back.

No reply.

"Erin? Are you goofing on us again?" I demanded.

Still no reply.

I could feel my throat tighten once again with fear. I walked over and pulled the string. My hand was shaking as I pulled it. I prayed silently to myself that Erin would return okay.

The light went out. The three of us waited tensely for Erin to come back.

After what seemed an endless wait, she shimmered back into view. She turned quickly away from the mirror, a triumphant smile on her face. "The new champ!" she declared, raising her fists in a gesture of victory.

"You're okay?" I asked, my feeling of fear refusing to leave.

She nodded. "Just fine, worrywart." She stepped away from the mirror, walking unsteadily.

I stared at her. Something about her looked different.

She looked perfectly okay. Not pale or sick-looking or anything. But something was different. Her smile? Her hair? I wished I could figure out what.

"Max, pull the string." Zack's eager voice jerked me away from my thoughts. "Let's go, man. I'm going for *fifteen* minutes."

"Okay. Get ready," I said, glancing at Erin as I grabbed for the string. She flashed me a reassuring smile.

But something about her smile was different.

Something.

But what?

I pulled the string. Zack vanished in the flash of bright light.

"Return of the Invisible Man!" he cried in a deep voice.

"Not so loud," I warned him. "My mom'll hear you downstairs."

Erin had lowered herself to the floor beside April. I walked over and stood over her. "You sure you're okay?" I asked. "You don't feel dizzy or weird or anything?"

She shook her head. "No. Really. Why don't you believe me, Max?"

As I stared down at her, I tried to figure out what was different about her appearance. What a mystery! I just couldn't put my finger on it.

"Well, how come you didn't answer when I called you?" I demanded.

"Huh?" Her face filled with surprise. "When?"

"At about twelve minutes," I told her. "I called you and Zack called you. But you didn't answer us."

Erin's expression turned thoughtful. "I guess I didn't hear you," she replied finally. "But I'm fine, Max. Really. I feel great. It was really awesome."

I joined them on the floor and leaned back against the wall to wait for Zack's turn to be over. "I really mean it. Don't turn off the light till fifteen minutes," he reminded me.

Then he messed up my hair, making it stand straight up in the air.

Both girls laughed.

I had to get up, walk over to the mirror, and comb it back down. I don't know why people think messed-up hair is such a riot. I really don't get it.

"Hey, follow me. I've got an idea," Zack said. His voice was coming from the doorway.

"Whoa — hold on!" I called. But I could hear his sneakers clomping across the attic.

"Follow me outside," he called to us. We heard his footsteps on the attic stairs.

"Zack — don't do it," I pleaded. "Whatever it is, don't do it!"

But there was no way he was going to listen to me.

A few seconds later, we were out the back door, following our invisible friend toward our neighbor Mr. Evander's back yard.

This is going to be trouble, I thought unhappily. Big trouble.

Erin, April, and I hid behind the hedge that separated our two yards. As usual, Mr. Evander was out in his tomato garden, stooped over, pulling up weeds, his big belly hanging out under his T-shirt, his red bald head shiny under the sun.

What is Zack going to do? I wondered, holding my breath, my whole body heavy with dread.

And then I saw three tomatoes float up from the ground. They hovered in the air, then floated closer to Mr. Evander.

Oh, no, I thought, groaning silently to myself. Please, Zack. Please don't do it.

Erin, April, and I were huddled together behind the hedge, staring in disbelief as the three tomatoes began to circle each other rapidly in the air.

Invisible Zack was juggling them. Showing off, as usual. He was always bragging about how he could juggle, and we couldn't.

It took a while for Mr. Evander to notice.

But when he finally saw the three tomatoes spinning around in midair a few feet in front of him, his eyes bugged out and his face turned as red as the tomatoes!

"Oh!" he cried. He let the weeds fall from his

hands. And then he just stared at the spinning tomatoes, like he was frozen.

Zack tossed the tomatoes higher as he juggled.

April and Erin held hands over their mouths to stifle their laughter. They thought Zack's stunt was a real hoot. But I just wanted to get Zack back up to the attic.

"Hey, Mary! Mary!" Mr. Evander started calling to his wife. "Mary — come out here! You've *got* to see this! Mary!"

A few seconds later, his wife came running across the yard, a frightened expression on her face. "Mike, what's wrong? What's *wrong*?"

"Look — these tomatoes are twirling in the air!" Mr. Evander cried, motioning wildly for her to hurry.

Zack let the tomatoes fall to the ground.

"Where?" Mrs. Evander asked breathlessly, running as fast as she could.

"There. Look!" Mr. Evander pointed.

"I don't see any tomatoes," Mrs. Evander said, stopping in front of her husband, panting loudly.

"Yes! They're spinning. They're — "

"Those tomatoes?" Mrs. Evander asked, pointing to the three tomatoes on the ground.

"Well . . . yes. They were twirling around, and — " Looking terribly confused, Mr. Evander scratched the back of his neck.

"Mike, how long have you been out in the sun?" his wife scolded. "Didn't I tell you to wear a cap?"

"Uh . . . I'll be in in a few minutes," Mr. Evander said softly, staring down at the tomatoes.

As soon as Mrs. Evander turned and headed back to the house, the three tomatoes floated up from the ground and began twirling in the air again.

"Mary, look!" Mr. Evander shouted excitedly. "Look — quick! They're doing it again!"

Zack let the tomatoes drop to the ground.

Mrs. Evander spun around and stared into empty space. "Mike, you'd better come with me — *right now*," she insisted. She hurried back, grabbed Mr. Evander by the arm, and pulled him away. The poor man looked totally bewildered, staring at the tomatoes on the ground, still scratching the back of his neck as his wife pulled him to the house.

"Hey, this is awesome!" Zack cried, right in front of me.

Erin and April collapsed in wild giggles. I had to admit it was pretty funny. We laughed about it for a while. Then we sneaked back into the house and up to the attic.

In the safety of the little room, we laughed some more about Zack's juggling stunt. Zack bragged that he was the world's first invisible juggler.

Then, at twelve minutes, Zack suddenly stopped answering us.

Just as Erin had.

The three of us called his name over and over.

Silence.

Zack didn't reply.

"I'm going to bring him back," I said, instantly gripped with fear once again. I ran to the string.

"Wait," Erin said, holding me back.

"Huh? What for?" I pulled away from her.

"He said to wait till fifteen minutes, remember?" she argued.

"Erin, he's completely disappeared!" I cried.

"But he'll be really mad," Erin pleaded.

"I say bring him back," April said anxiously.

"Give him until fifteen minutes," Erin insisted.

"No," I said. I pulled the string.

The light clicked off.

A few minutes later, Zack flickered back. He smiled at us. "How long?" he asked, turning to April.

"Thirteen minutes, twenty seconds," she told him.

His grin widened. "The new champ!"

"You're okay? You didn't answer us," I said, studying his face.

"I'm fine. I didn't hear you calling me. But I'm fine."

Zack looked different to me, too. Something was very different about him. But what?

"What's your problem, Max?" he demanded. "Why are you staring at me like I'm some kind of alien life-form or something?"

"Your hair," I said, studying him. "Was it like that before?"

"Huh? What are you talking about? Are you freaking out or something?" Zack asked, rolling his eyes.

"Was your hair like that before?" I repeated. "Buzzed real short on the right and then combed long to the left? Wasn't it the other way around?"

"You're messed up, Max," he said, grinning at Erin and April. "My hair is the same it's always been. You've been staring in that mirror too long or something."

I could've sworn his hair had been short on the left, long on the right. But I guess Zack would know his own hair.

"Are you going to go?" Erin asked, jumping up behind me.

"Yeah, are you going to beat fifteen minutes?" Zack asked.

I shook my head. "No, I really don't feel like it," I told them truthfully. "Let's declare Zack the winner and get out of here."

"No way!" Zack and Erin declared in unison.

"You've got to try," Zack insisted.

"Don't wimp out, Max. You can beat Zack. I know you can," Erin declared.

She and Zack both pushed me up to the mirror.

I tried to pull back. But they practically held me in place.

"No. Really," I said. "Zack can be the winner. I — "

"Go for it, Max!" Erin urged. "I'm betting on you!"

"Yeah. Go for it," Zack repeated, his hand firmly on my shoulder.

"No. Please — " I said.

But Zack reached up with his free hand and pulled the string.

21

I stared into the mirror for a moment, waiting for the glare to fade from my eyes. It was always such a shock. That first moment, when your reflection disappeared. When you stared at the spot where you knew you were standing — and realized you were looking right through yourself!

"How do you feel, Max? How do you feel?" Erin asked, imitating me.

"Erin, what's your problem?" I snapped. It wasn't like her to be so sarcastic.

"Just giving you a taste of your own medicine," she replied, grinning.

Something about her smile was lopsided, not normal.

"Think you can beat my record?" Zack demanded.

"I don't know. Maybe," I replied uncertainly.

Zack stepped up to the mirror and studied his reflection. I had the strangest feeling as I watched him. I can't really explain it. I'd never seen Zack stand in just that position and admire himself in just that way.

Something was different. I knew it. But I couldn't figure out what.

Maybe it's just my nervousness, I told myself.

I'm just so stressed out. Maybe it's affecting the way I look at my friends. Maybe I'm making all this up.

"Two minutes," April announced.

"Are you just going to stand there?" Erin asked, staring into the mirror. "Aren't you going to move around or anything, Max?"

"No. I don't think so," I said. "I mean, I can't think of anything I want to do. I'm just going to wait till the time is up."

"You want to quit now?" Zack asked, grinning at the spot where he thought I was standing.

I shook my head. Then I remembered that no one could see it. "No. I might as well go the distance," I told him. "Since I'm here, I might as well make you look bad, Zack."

He laughed scornfully. "You won't beat thirteen-twenty," he said confidently. "No way."

"Well, you know what?" I said, angered by his smug tone of voice. "I'm just going to stand here until I do."

And that's what I did. I stood in place, leaning against the mirror frame, while April counted off the minutes.

I did okay until a short while after she had called

out eleven minutes. Then, suddenly, the glare of the light began to hurt my eyes.

I closed my eyes, but it didn't help. The light grew brighter, harsher. It seemed to sweep around me, surround me, fold over me.

And then I began to feel dizzy and light. As if I were about to float away, even though I knew I was standing in place.

"Hey, guys?" I called out. "I think I've had enough."

My voice sounded tiny and far away, even to me.

The light swirled around me. I felt myself grow lighter, lighter, until I had to struggle to keep my feet on the floor to keep from floating away.

I uttered a high-pitched cry. I was suddenly gripped by panic.

Cold panic.

"Zack — bring me back!" I shouted.

"Okay, Max. No problem," I heard Zack reply.

He seemed miles and miles away.

I struggled to see him through the blinding yellow light. He was a dark figure behind the wall of light, a dark figure moving quickly to the mirror.

"I'm bringing you back now, Max. Hold on," I heard Zack say.

The bright light glowed even brighter. It hurt so much. Even with my eyes closed, it hurt.

"Zack, pull the string!" I shouted.

I opened my eyes to see his dim shadow reaching up to the string.

Pull it, pull it, *pull it*! I urged silently.

I knew that in a second, the light would go off. And I'd be safe.

A second.

One tug of the string.

Pull it, pull it, *pull it, Zack!*

Zack reached for the string. I saw him grab it.

And then I heard another voice in the room. A new voice. A surprised voice.

"Hi. What's going on up here? What are you kids doing?"

I saw the shadowy figure of Zack drop the string and step away without pulling it.

My mom had burst into the room.

22

"Please — pull the string!" I called.

No one seemed to hear me.

"We're just hanging out," I heard Zack tell my mom.

"But where's Max?" I heard her ask. "How did you find this little room? What are you all *doing* in here?" Her voice sounded as if it were coming from underwater, far, far away.

The entire room began to shimmer in the light, flickering on and off. I held on tightly to the frame of the mirror, struggling not to float away.

"Can you hear me?" I called. "Please, some-body — pull the string! Bring me back!"

They were just gray shadows in the wavering, rolling light. They didn't seem to hear me.

Gripping the frame tightly, I saw a shadow ap-proach the mirror. My mom. She walked around it, admiring it.

"I can't *believe* we never knew about this room.

393

Where did this old mirror come from?" I heard her ask.

She was standing so close to me. They all were.

They were so close and so far away at the same time.

"Please bring me back!" I shouted.

I listened for an answer. But the voices faded away.

The shadows moved in a flickering blur. I tried to reach out to them, but they were too far away.

I let go of the mirror frame and began to float.

"Mom, I'm right here. Can't you hear me? Can't you *do* anything?"

So light, so completely weightless, I floated in front of the mirror.

My feet were off the floor. I couldn't see them in the blinding glare.

I floated to the mirror glass, under the light.

I could feel the light pull me closer. Closer.

Until it pulled me right into the mirror.

I knew I was inside the mirror. Inside a glistening blur of colors. The shapes shimmered and rolled together as if underwater.

And I floated through the glimmering shards of light and color, floated silently away from my friends, away from my mom, floated away from the tiny attic room.

Into the center of the mirror.

Into the center of an undulating, rolling world of twisting lights and colors.

"Help me!" I cried.

But my voice was muffled by the blurred, shifting colors.

"Bring me back! Get me back!"

Floating deeper into this glimmering world, I could barely hear myself.

Deeper into the mirror. And still deeper.

The colors gave way to shapes of gray and black. It was cold here. Cold as glass.

And as I floated deeper, deeper, the grays and blacks faded, too. The world was white now. Pure white all around. Shadowless white as far as I could see.

I stared straight ahead, no longer calling out, too frightened to call out, too mystified by the cold, ivory world I had entered.

"Hello, Max," a familiar voice said.

"Ohh!" I cried out, realizing I was not alone.

23

A scream of terror escaped my lips. I tried to form words, but my brain seemed to be paralyzed.

The figure approached quickly, silently, through the cold, white world of the mirror. He smiled at me, an eerie, familiar smile.

"You!" I managed to scream.

He stopped inches away from me.

I stared at him in disbelief.

I was staring at myself. Me. Smiling back at me. The smile as cold as the glass that surrounded us.

"Don't be afraid," he said. "I'm your reflection."

"No!"

His eyes — *my* eyes — studied me hungrily, like a dog staring at a meaty bone. His smile grew wider as I cried out my fear.

"I've been waiting here for you," my reflection said, his eyes locked on mine.

"No!" I repeated.

I turned away.

I knew I had to get away.

I started to run.

But I stopped short when I saw the faces in front of me. Distorted, unhappy faces, dozens of them, fun house mirror faces, with enormous, drooping eyes, and tiny mouths tight with sadness.

The faces seemed to hover just ahead of me. The gaping eyes staring at me, the tiny mouths moving rapidly as if calling to me, warning me, telling me to get away.

Who were these people, these faces?

Why were they inside the mirror with me?

Why did their distorted, twisted images reveal so much sadness, so much pain?

"No!"

I gasped as I thought I recognized two of the floating faces, their mouths working furiously, their eyebrows rising wildly up and down.

Erin and Zack?

No.

That was impossible, wasn't it?

I stared hard at them. Why were they talking so frantically? What were they trying to tell me?

"Help me!" I called. But they didn't seem to hear me.

The faces, dozens of them, bobbed and floated.

"Help me — please!"

And then I felt myself being spun around. I stared into the eyes of my reflection as he gripped my shoulders and held me in place.

"You're not leaving," he told me. His quiet voice echoed through the clear stillness, icicles scratching against glass.

I struggled to free myself, but his grip was strong.

"I'm the one to leave," he told me. "I've been waiting so long. Ever since you turned on the light. And now I'm going to step out from here and join the others."

"Others?" I cried.

"Your friends gave in easily," he said. "They did not resist. The switch was made. And now you and I will also make a switch."

"No!" I screamed, and my cry seemed to echo through the icy cold for miles.

"Why are you so afraid?" he asked, turning me around, still gripping my shoulders, bringing his face close to mine. "Are you so afraid of your other side, Max?"

He stared at me intently. "That's what I am, you know," he said. "I am your reflection. Your other side. Your cold side. Don't be afraid of me. Your friends were not afraid. They made the switch without much of a struggle. Now they are inside the mirror. And their reflections . . ."

His voice trailed off. He didn't have to finish his sentence. I knew what he was saying.

Now I understood about Erin and Zack. Now I understood why they looked different to me.

They were reversed. They were their own reflections.

And now I understood why they pushed me into the mirror, why they forced me to disappear, too.

If I didn't do something, I realized, my reflection would switch places with me. My reflection would step into the attic. And I'd be trapped inside the mirror forever, trapped forever with the sad, bobbing faces.

But what could I do?

Staring at myself, I decided to stall, to ask questions, to give myself a little time to think.

"Whose mirror is it? Who built it?" I demanded.

He shrugged. "How should I know? I'm only your reflection, remember?"

"But how — "

"It's time," he said eagerly. "Don't try to stall with foolish questions. Time to make the switch. Time for *you* to become *my* reflection!

24

I pulled away.

I started to run.

The sad, distorted faces hovered in front of me.

I shut my eyes and dodged away from them.

I couldn't think. Couldn't breathe.

My legs pumped. My arms flew out at my sides. It was so clear and bright, I couldn't tell if I was moving or not. My feet couldn't feel a floor. There were no walls, no ceiling. There was no *air* brushing my face as I ran.

But my fear kept me moving. Through the clear, cold, shimmering light.

He was behind me.

I couldn't hear him.

He had no shadow.

But I knew he was right behind me.

And I knew that if he caught me, I'd be lost. Lost inside this blank world, unable to see, to hear, to smell, to touch anything, lost in the cold glass forever.

Another silent, bobbing face.

And so I kept running.

Until the colors returned.

Until light bent to form shapes.

And I saw shadows moving and shifting in front of me.

"Stop, Max!" I heard my reflection's voice right behind me. "Stop right there!"

But now *he* sounded worried.

And so I kept running, running into the colors and moving shapes.

Suddenly, Zack turned off the light.

I came bursting out of the mirror, into the tiny attic room, into an explosion of sound, of color, of hard surfaces, of real things. The real world.

I stood up, panting, gasping for breath. I tested my legs. I stomped on the floor. The solid floor.

I turned my eyes to my friends, who were standing in front of me, startled expressions on their faces. My mom, I realized, must have retreated back downstairs.

"Did you make the switch?" Zack asked eagerly, his eyes glowing with excitement.

"Are you one of us?" Erin asked at the same time.

"No," said a voice — my voice — coming from just behind me.

We all stared into the mirror.

Inside it, my reflection, red-faced and angry, glared out at us, his hands pressed against the glass. "He got away," my reflection told my friends. "The switch wasn't made."

"I don't understand!" I heard April cry. "What's going on, guys?"

Zack and Erin ignored her. They stepped up quickly and grabbed me by the arms. They spun me around roughly.

"The switch wasn't made," my reflection repeated from inside the glass.

"No problem," Erin told it.

She and Zack forced me up to the mirror.

"You're going back in, Max," Zack said heatedly.

He reached up and pulled the light cord.

25

The light flashed on.

I went invisible.

My reflection remained in the mirror, open palms pressed against the inside of the glass, staring out.

"I'm waiting for you, Max," he said. "In a few minutes, you'll join me in here."

"No!" I shouted. "I'm leaving. I'm going downstairs."

"No, you're not," my reflection said, shaking his head. "Erin and Zack won't let you escape. But don't be so frightened, Max. It's all quite painless. Really." He smiled. It was my smile. But it was cold. Cruel.

"I don't get this," April was protesting back by the door. "Will someone tell me what's going on?"

"You'll see, April," Erin told her soothingly.

What am I going to do? I wondered, frozen in panic.

What *can* I do?

"Just a few more minutes," my reflection said calmly, already celebrating his victory. His freedom.

"April, get help!" I cried.

She spun around at the sound of my voice. "Huh?"

"Get help! Go downstairs. Get help! Hurry!" I screamed.

"But — I don't understand — " April hesitated.

Erin and Zack moved to block her path.

But the door suddenly swung open.

I saw Lefty stop at the doorway. He peered in. Saw my reflection.

He must have thought the reflection was me.

"Think fast!" he shouted, and he tossed a softball.

The ball smashed into the mirror.

I saw the startled look on Lefty's face. And then I heard the crash and saw the mirror crack and shatter.

My reflection didn't have time to react. He broke into shards of glass and fell to the floor.

"Nooooo!" Erin and Zack shrieked.

I popped back into view just as Erin's and Zack's reflections floated up off the floor. They were sucked into the broken mirror — screaming all the way — sucked into it as if a powerful vacuum cleaner were pulling them in.

The two reflections flew screaming into the mirror and appeared to crack into hundreds of pieces.

"Whoa!" Lefty cried, gripping the door with all his strength, pressing his body against the doorframe, struggling to keep himself from being sucked into the room.

And then Erin and Zack dropped onto the floor on their knees, looking dazed and confused, staring at the pieces of shattered mirror that littered the floor around them.

"You're back!" I cried happily. "It's really you!"

"Yeah. It's me," Zack said, climbing unsteadily to his feet, then turning to help Erin up.

The mirror was shattered. The reflections were gone.

Erin and Zack gazed around the room, still shaken and dazed.

April stared at me in total confusion.

Lefty remained outside the doorway, shaking his head. "Max," he said, "you should've caught the ball. That was an easy catch."

Erin and Zack were back. And they were okay.

It didn't take long to get everything back to normal.

We explained everything to April and Lefty as best we could.

April went home. She had to baby-sit her little sister.

Erin and Zack — the *real* Erin and Zack — helped me sweep up the broken glass. Then we closed the door to the little room. I latched it tightly, and we all carried cartons over and stacked them up to block off the door.

We knew we'd never go in there again.

We vowed never to tell anyone about getting invisible or the mirror or what happened in that little room. Then Erin and Zack headed home.

Later, Lefty and I were hanging around out in the back yard. "That was so scary," I told Lefty with a shudder. "You just can't imagine what it was like."

"Sounds pretty scary," Lefty replied absently. He tossed his softball from hand to hand. "But at least everything is okay now. Want to play a little catch?"

"No," I shook my head. I wasn't in the mood. But then I changed my mind. "Maybe it'll take my mind off what happened this morning," I said.

Lefty tossed me the ball. We trotted behind the garage, our usual place for tossing the ball around.

I lobbed it back to him.

We were having a pretty good game of catch.

Until about five minutes had gone by.

Until . . .

Until I stopped and froze in place.

Were my eyes playing tricks on me?

"Here comes my fastball," he said. He heaved it at me.

No. No. No.

I gaped open-mouthed as the ball shot past me.
I didn't even try to catch it. I couldn't move.
I could only stare in horror.
My brother was throwing right-handed.

R.L. STINE is the author of the series Fear Street, Nightmare Room, and Give Yourself Goosebumps, as well as the phenomenally successful Goosebumps series. His thrilling teen titles have sold more than 250 million copies internationally—enough to earn him a spot in the *Guinness Book of World Records*! Mr. Stine lives in New York City with his wife, Jane, and his son, Matt.